MW00845939

CHES® Exam Review

Certification Guide for Health Education Specialists

Elizabeth M. Felter, DrPH, MCHES
Jason Flatt, PhD, MCHES

SPRINGER PUBLISHING COMPANY

Copyright © 2019 Springer Publishing Company, LLC

All rights reserved.

No part of this publication may be reproduced, stored in a retrieval system, or transmitted in any form or by any means, electronic, mechanical, photocopying, recording, or otherwise, without the prior permission of Springer Publishing Company, LLC, or authorization through payment of the appropriate fees to the Copyright Clearance Center, Inc., 222 Rosewood Drive, Danvers, MA 01923, 978-750-8400, fax 978-646-8600, info@copyright.com or on the Web at www.copyright.com.

Springer Publishing Company, LLC
11 West 42nd Street
New York, NY 10036
www.springerpub.com

Acquisitions Editor: David D'Addona
Compositor: diacriTech

ISBN: 978-0-8261-3375-5
ebook ISBN: 978-0-8261-3376-2

21 22 / 6

Content from *A Competency Based Framework for Health Education Specialists – 2015*, including the CHES registered trademark in the title and Area of Responsibility and 2015 Competency and Sub-competency nomenclature are reprinted by permission of The National Commission for Health Education Credentialing, Inc., and the Society for Public Health Education.

The author and the publisher of this work have made every effort to use sources believed to be reliable to provide information that is accurate and compatible with the standards generally accepted at the time of publication. The author and publisher shall not be liable for any special, consequential, or exemplary damages resulting, in whole or in part, from the readers' use of, or reliance on, the information contained in this book. The publisher has no responsibility for the persistence or accuracy of URLs for external or third-party Internet websites referred to in this publication and does not guarantee that any content on such websites is, or will remain, accurate or appropriate.

Library of Congress Cataloging-in-Publication Data
Names: Felter, Elizabeth M. (Elizabeth Madison), author. | Flatt, Jason, author.
Title: Certified health education specialist (CHES) exam study guide / Elizabeth M. Felter, Jason Flatt.
Description: New York, NY : Springer Publishing Company, LLC, [2019] | Includes bibliographical references.
Identifiers: LCCN 2018013502| ISBN 9780826133755 | ISBN 9780826133762 (e-book)
Subjects: | MESH: Health Educators | Health Education | Certification | Clinical Competence | Examination Questions
Classification: LCC R834.5 | NLM W 18.2 | DDC 610.76—dc23
LC record available at https://lccn.loc.gov/2018013502

Contact us to receive discount rates on bulk purchases.
We can also customize our books to meet your needs.
For more information please contact: sales@springerpub.com

Printed in the United States of America.

This book is dedicated to
Robert Kyle and Eleanor Rose.

Contents

Acknowledgments

This book would not have been possible without the help of many people. We are grateful to Dr. Patricia Documét and Dr. Steve Albert of the Department of Behavioral and Community Sciences and Ms. Linda Duchak and the Center for Public Health Practice at the University of Pittsburgh for contributing questions for the guide. We would also like to thank Ms. Joan Anson, Director of Career Services at the Graduate School of Public Health at the University of Pittsburgh, for her contributions in Chapter 10. Our thanks go as well to Ms. Heidi Hauser Green for her editorial work. Finally, our eternal gratitude to Dr. Beth Madison and Dr. Carol Christen; without them this book would not have been possible.

Chapter 1

So You Want to Take the CHES® Exam?

INTRODUCTION

In this chapter, we talk about the things you need to know before you take the Certified Health Education Specialist (CHES®) exam. First, we briefly explain the CHES® credential. Second, we go over who is eligible for the CHES® exam and how you can confirm with the National Commission for Health Education Credentialing, Inc. that you are eligible to sit the exam. Then we will walk you through the process of applying for the exam. Finally, we describe what the day of the exam is like, what to expect, and give you some strategies to make sure it goes as smoothly as possible.

A BRIEF REVIEW OF THE CHES® CREDENTIAL

Chances are, if you are reading this guide, you already have some idea about the CHES® credential. So if you feel you are already knowledgable in this area, feel free to skip ahead! But maybe someone just said to you, "You should really take the CHES® exam," or you have noticed that many of the jobs you want to apply for say "CHES® preferred" and you want to learn a bit more. So let us start at the beginning:

In 1978, the National Task Force on the Preparation & Practice of Health Educators was established and over the next decade it worked to develop and promote the Framework for the Development of Competency-Based Curricula for Entry Level Health Educators. Ten years later, in 1988, it became a nonprofit organization, the National Commission for Health Education Credentialing, Inc (NCHEC)—the name it retains today. In 1990 they administered the first CHES® exam, and 8 years later they began offering the exam twice yearly, as it remains today. In 2008, the credential was accredited by the National Commission on Certifying Agencies (NCCA), and it was reaccredited in 2013. In 2011, NCHEC began offering the Master Certified Health Education Specialist (MCHES®) credential for advanced-level practitioners. We talk more about the MCHES® in Chapter 10.

So, that is the history. But what is a CHES®, exactly? The CHES® credential identifies you as a Certified Health Education Specialist[1]. That means you have been certified by NCHEC as a health educator. But then, what is a health educator?

O*Net Online (2017) defines health educators as those who "provide and manage health education programs that help individuals, families, and their communities maximize and maintain healthy lifestyles. Collect and analyze data to identify community needs prior to planning, implementing, monitoring, and evaluating programs designed to encourage healthy lifestyles, policies, and environments. May serve as a resource to assist individuals, other healthcare workers, or the community, and may administer fiscal resources for health education programs."

According to a DOL report in May 2017:

- There were an estimated 58,040 health educators working in the United States.
- Employment opportunities for health educators were projected to grow by 16% from 2016 to 2026, "much faster" than the average for all occupations.
- Nearly half of health educators work in healthcare or social assistance organizations.
- Approximately 22% of health educators work in the government sector.

Conduct a Community Health Needs Assessment ⟶ Plan Program ⟶ Implement Program ⟶ Monitor program ⟶ Evaluate Program

CHES® EXAM ELIGIBILITY

Before proceeding further, it is crucial to ascertain if you are eligible to take the CHES® exam. There are two basic requirements to be accepted to take the examination: You must hold at least a bachelor's degree from an

---

[1] A word about terminology: NCHEC uses the term "Health Education Specialist," and the Bureau of Labor Statistics (and others) use the term "Health Educator." We will use the terms interchangeably in this book.

accredited institution of higher education, and you must submit an official academic transcript to NCHEC that shows you majored in some form of health education.

But wait—my degree doesn't say that!

Do not panic! NCHEC will also accept an official transcript that reflects at least 25 semester hours or 37 quarter hours of course work (with a grade of "C" or better) with specific preparation addressing the Seven Areas of Responsibility for Health Education Specialists.

WHAT ARE THE SEVEN AREAS OF RESPONSIBILITY FOR HEALTH EDUCATION SPECIALISTS?

We are glad you asked. These are important to understand, as they form the basis of the CHES® credential:

Area I: Assess Needs, Resources, and Capacity for Health Education/Promotion

Area II: Plan Health Education/Promotion

Area III: Implement Health Education/Promotion

Area IV: Conduct Evaluation and Research Related to Health Education/Promotion

Area V: Administer and Manage Health Education/Promotion

Area VI: Serve as a Health Education/Promotion Resource Person

Area VII: Communicate, Promote, and Advocate for Health, Health Education/Promotion, and the Profession

From there it gets a bit more complicated, but we will walk you through it. A minimum of 12 semester hours/18 quarter hours must be from process courses that clearly align with the Seven Areas of Responsibility. Those courses might be called Program Planning, Program Evaluation, Research Methods, or Statistics, for example. As many as (but no more than) 9 semester hours/14 quarter hours may be from topic-focused courses that include elements contained in the Seven Areas of Responsibility, such as Health Communications and Worksite Health Promotion. Finally, as many as 6 semester hours/8 quarter hours may be from other courses that include elements contained in the Seven

Areas of Responsibility. Here you have a bit more flexibility, but the course has to be related to one of the Seven Areas—a budgeting class, for example.

So, look at your transcript. Identify the 25 hours you think apply to the Seven Areas. Then make sure at least 12 hours are method related, no more than nine are topic focused, and no more than six are related to—but not wholly about—the Seven Areas of Responsibility. You can use this handy worksheet to organize your thoughts (Figure 1.1):

Worksheet for identifying qualifying credits for the CHES® exam
Must contain:
- 12 semester hours (18 quarter hours) from Process courses that align with the Seven Areas of Responsibility
- 9 hours (14 quarter hours) (max) of Topic-focused courses
- 6 semester hours (8 quarter hours) from other courses that include elements contained in the Seven Areas.

As a reminder, the Seven Areas of Responsibility are:

Area I: Assess Needs, Assets, and Capacity for Health Education
Area II: Plan Health Education
Area III: Implement Health Education
Area IV: Conduct Evaluation and Research Related to Health Education
Area V: Administer and Manage Health Education
Area VI: Serve as a Health Education Resource Person
Area VII: Communicate, Promote, and Advocate for Health, Health Education/Promotion, and the Profession

Example:

Course Name	Number of Credit Hours from Process Courses	Number of Credit Hours from Topic-focused Courses	Number of Credit Hours from other Courses related to the Seven Areas	
Program Planning and Evaluation	3			
Epidemiology	3			
Health Theories	3			
Public Health Research Methods	3			
Maternal and Child Health		3		
Social Marketing		3		
Health Care Policy		3		
Health Literacy			3	
Health Communications			3	
Totals	12	9	6	
Grand Total:				27 hours

Figure 1.1a Sample worksheet

Now here's a worksheet for your classes:

Course Name	Number of Credit Hours from Process Courses	Number of Credit Hours from Topic-focused Courses	Number of Credit Hours from other courses related to the Seven Areas	
Totals				
Grand Total:				_____ hours

Figure 1.1b Worksheet for identifying qualifying credits for the CHES® exam

If your degree is called "Health Behavior and Health Education," "Health Promotion and Behavior," "Behavioral and Community Health Sciences," or anything similar, you are probably OK. However, NCHEC does not refund your money if you apply for the exam and you do not actually qualify to take it. So it pays to be sure. You can check with your school to see if students with your degree or major have successfully taken the exam (talking to someone in Career Services might be a good place to start). But individuals can take different classes even within the same major, so you will want to confirm your particular course load with the stated requirements to make sure you qualify.

PRESCREEN OR NOT? UNDERSTANDING THE PRESCREENING OPTION

The best way to make sure that you are qualified to take the CHES® exam is to take advantage of NCHEC's Prescreen Service. Fill out the NCHEC's prescreen request form and submit it along with your official academic transcript(s) and a (nonrefundable) $25 fee. NCHEC will review your transcript(s) to determine if you are eligible. If you are missing certain classes, they will be identified and you will receive feedback on what you need to add to be eligible to sit the exam. If you do qualify to take the exam, NCHEC will credit the $25 you paid toward your exam fee. If you are unsure, it really pays to opt for the prescreen! It would be much better to lose $25 than the $100 nonrefundable application fee if it turns out you are not qualified! And the prescreening service has an additional benefit. The Prescreen Schedule is November 1 to February 1 for the April exam and May 1 to August 1 for the October exam, which may give current students time to register for any classes they are missing in time to take the exam for the next cycle. Say, for example, that you were hoping to take the exam in April with the 90-day option (more on that in a minute). You request a prescreen early in October and NCHEC tells you that you have only 9 of the required 12-semester hours of Process classes. That should leave you time to sign up for a Program Planning class (or something similar) in the spring semester. Problem solved, and the $25 you spent for prescreening can be applied to your exam. Bottom line: If you are unsure, prescreen!

APPLYING TO TAKE THE EXAM

Once you are sure you are eligible to take the exam, it is time to apply! The application process is fairly simple and can be completed online at www. nchec.org. If you prefer not to apply online, you can download a PDF of the application, fill it out, and mail it in or, if you are really old school, you can request an application packet to be mailed to you by calling the NCHEC office at (888) 624-3248. The application process is handled through an online portal through which you will create a username and password.

EXAM DATES

The CHES® exam is offered twice every year, in April and October. If you are graduating in the semester in which you wish to take the exam, you may apply for the 90-Day Eligibility Option. To qualify for this option, a student must be enrolled in an accredited institution of higher education and must submit an official transcript showing a minimum of 25 semester hours relating to the Seven Areas of Responsibility along with written verification from a faculty advisor assuring the student will complete all the degree requirements within 90 days of the exam date. The advantages of taking the exam during your last semester are that you are still in "school mode"—the information from your classes is fresh in your mind and you are used to taking exams, to say nothing of being able to start your job search with a brand new credential (and perhaps best of all, no more test-taking after you graduate!). There are some downsides, too: you may be already overwhelmed with finishing a thesis, studying for finals, and applying for jobs. You certainly do not want to jeopardize your final semester's grades (and possibly graduation) with another exam to study for. So if preparing for the CHES® exam is going to place too heavy a burden on you, remember that it will be offered again in 6 months. If you do choose the 90-Day Eligibility Option, NCHEC will withhold your credential until it receives your final transcripts.

EXAM FEES

The current exam fee schedule and structure has recently been simplified. See the following section for registration dates and fees for October and April dates (schedule/fees as of February 2018).

As in so many other situations, if you procrastinate in applying for the CHES® exam, it is going to cost you. The current fee schedule is in the following tables.

Of course, these deadlines and fees can change, so be sure to check with NCHEC before you make any plans.

Once your application is received and approved, you will receive instructions in the mail for scheduling your test. According to the NCHEC website, it is important to schedule your test as soon as possible, so do so as soon as your materials arrive.

October CHES® Exam	Nonstudent Fee	*Student Fee
Early Bird Registration: May 1–31	$270	$220
Regular Registration: June 1–July 31	$320	$270
Final (Late) Registration Deadline: August 31	$370	$320

April CHES® exam:	Nonstudent Fee	*Student Fee
Early Bird Registration: November 1–January 30	$270	$220
Regular Registration: December 1–January 31	$320	$270
Final (Late) Registration Deadline: February 28	$370	$320

* To qualify for the Student Fee rate you must be enrolled in 9 or more credit hours the semester you apply for the exam (12 or more quarter hours) and/or provide documentation from your college/university of your full-time status.

A word on address changes: NCHEC will only send test results to the address it has on file. So if you move, make sure to log on to the NCHEC website and update your contact information or call the office as soon as you know your new address.

DAY OF TESTING–SCHEDULE AND ADVICE

Starting in October of 2018, instead of only being able to take the exam on one of the two Saturdays offered a year, there will be an extended range of dates and testing locations available each April and October—NCHEC is currently advertising at least 410 testing sites in the United States and many more internationally. You will also immediately get an unofficial pass/fail score rather than waiting 4 to 6 weeks to find out if you passed. All of this means it will be more convenient to take the CHES® exam—good news for future CHES® applicants!

The day of testing will go much more smoothly if you have some idea what to expect. According to the Prometric website, this is the check-in procedure:

- Original, valid (unexpired), government-issued photo and signature-bearing identification is required to take an exam. NCHEC will determine which IDs are acceptable and communicate that to you prior to the test.

- You will be scanned with a metal detector wand **prior to every entry** into the test room.

- You will be required to raise your pants legs above your ankles, empty, and turn all pockets inside-out and raise shirt sleeves above your wrists **prior to every entry** into the test room.

- If you are wearing eyeglasses, you will be required to remove them for visual inspection to ensure they do not contain a recording device. Large jewelry items must be stored in your locker due to concerns over concealed recording devices.

Prometric offers the *Test Drive* program, which, for a fee, allows those scheduled for a test to go to the center on a day before the exam and complete a "dry run" of the check-in, security, and testing procedures. According to its website, familiarity with the location and procedures of the exam will allow you to be better prepared on the actual exam day. For more information on Prometric and testing procedures please visit www.prometric.com. Please check with NCHEC for updates or changes to these procedures—it will always have the most up-to-date information.

TEST DAY: QUESTIONS AND ANSWERS

Q: What can I bring to the exam?

A: Not much. PURSES, FOOD, DRINKS, COATS, CELL PHONES, AND SO ON, WILL NOT BE ALLOWED AT YOUR SEAT. There will be lockers available to store those things, but it is best to leave as much in your car or at home as possible. All you may have at your seat are site-issued tissues and soft earplugs (without cords).

Q: How can I keep track of time?

A: You may not wear a watch. Presumably, the computer screen will keep time for you.

Q: How long is the exam?

A: Three hours. (and 165 questions)

Q: What if I have to go to the bathroom?

A: Exams may have scheduled or unscheduled breaks, as determined by NCHEC. Each time you leave the test room, you must sign out. The testing center attendant will inform you of what is permitted during exam breaks, specifically whether access to your locker, and to the cell phone and notes within it, is allowed. All candidates must inform the testing center attendant

before accessing a stored item—including medicine—during a break. Upon return from a break, without exception, you must go through all security checks, present valid ID, sign in, and, if required by the test sponsor, provide a fingerprint to be readmitted to the test room. Remember, the clock does not stop while you are out of the hall, so go quickly! Repeated or lengthy departures from the test room will be reported to NCHEC.

Q: What if I do not understand a question?

A: If there is a mechanical problem with the computer (screen freezes or goes dark, etc.), inform the testing center attendant. If you do not understand the wording of a question or are not sure of an answer, the testing center attendant or fellow test takers cannot help you. Remember, 15 of the 165 questions are pretest questions, and the question that is stumping you could be one of those on the pretest. Just answer as best as you can and move on.

Q: Is there a penalty for guessing?

A: No. So do not leave a question unanswered! There are generally four potential multiple choice answers, so even a random guess has a 25% chance of being right. If you can eliminate one or two of the answers, your odds are even higher. So do not leave anything blank!

Q: What if I finish the exam before the 3 hours are up?

A: Follow the on-screen prompts or the directions of the testing center administrator, who will collect all the testing material (including scratch paper, if it is available). You are then free to leave—but you may not come back, so take time to check your work and make sure you are really done!

AFTER THE TEST: QUESTIONS AND ANSWERS

Q: What is the pass rate for the CHES® Exam?

A: It varies. According to NCHEC, it uses a criterion-referenced passing point technique that is an industry standard. Since there are multiple versions of the exam offered each year, the pass rate is slightly different for each one. For the two exams in 2017, the pass rate was between 60.22% and 69.29%.

Q: What if my address changes after I take the exam but before results are mailed?

A: Inform NCHEC on its website or call the office. Make sure you forward your mail through the U.S. Postal Service.

CONCLUSION

Now that we have walked you through the process of applying for, taking, and waiting for the results of the CHES® exam, let us move on to reviewing the material that may be covered on the exam. Chapter 2 will start with Area I: Assess Needs, Resources, and Capacity for Health Education/Promotion.

REFERENCE

O*Net Online. (2017). Summary report for: 2101091.00—Health educators. Retrieved from https://www.onetonline.org/link/summary/21-1091.00

Chapter 2

Area I: Assess Needs, Resources, and Capacity for Health Education/Promotion

[handwritten annotations:]

Needs Assessment
— Health knowledge
— Perception
— Attitude
— Motivations
— Practices
SE Environment

individual use qualit and quanti data — survey, questionnaire, focus groups, interviews

Capacity Assessment
Does community have capacity to provide interventions developed by the health program

INTRODUCTION

This chapter covers how to assess needs, assets, and capacity for health education. Health education specialists need to develop skills in using existing data as well as analyzing and interpreting findings from data. This chapter also focuses on conducting needs assessments and potential barriers and facilitators to health education programs.

★ Needs assessments are often one of the first strategies used by health educators to better understand the needs, interests, extent of health problems, as well as available resources. According to the National Commission for Health Education Credentialing (NCHEC), Society for Public Health Education (SOPHE), and American Association for Health Education (AAHE), a key area of responsibility for entry- and advanced-level health educators is the assessment of individual and community needs for health education. This includes obtaining health-related data, distinguishing between behaviors that enhance and impede well-being, and understanding the needs for health education. Needs assessment should be a part of both program planning and evaluation.

⭐NEEDS ASSESSMENTS AND CAPACITY BUILDING ARE ESSENTIAL PARTS OF PLANNING FOR HEALTH EDUCATION

— The purpose of a needs assessment is to gather information in order to determine what health education activities may be most appropriate given the needs and setting. Needs assessments ask about the most important needs of an individual or group.

— A needs assessment is a systematic, planned collection of information about the health knowledge, perceptions, attitudes, motivation, and practices of individuals or groups and the quality of the socioeconomic environment they live in; it is the process to address the gap between what is and what should be (Aday & Cornelius, 2011). A needs assessment can also be used during the evaluation stage of a health education program to monitor program impact.

Goals of a needs assessment include identifying and prioritizing health problems, prioritizing the strategies that will be most appropriate for addressing the identified health problems, and identifying resources that will support addressing the identified health problems (Gilmore, 2012).

What is the problem
Strategies to solve problem
Resources to solve problem

A needs assessment can involve using qualitative or quantitative (mixed method) methodologies in order to uncover the health knowledge, perceptions, attitudes, motivation...etc of individuals and communities and the socioeconomic environment they live

Assessing Capacity

Capacity is defined as both individual and collective resources that can be utilized for health enhancement. Assessing capacity involves identifying areas that may need to be enhanced prior to implementing a health education program in order to ensure that the program can be sustained long term. This includes examining potential assets at the individual, group, and community levels. A capacity assessment measures actual or potential resources that can aid in the maintenance and enhancement of health education programs. For example, the Centers for Disease Control and Prevention (CDC) Diabetes Prevention Recognition Programs utilize capacity assessments to determine whether organizations have the capacity to deliver approved type 2 diabetes-prevention lifestyle interventions. This includes the identifying eligible participants from a community (individual level), assessing whether the organization's staff have the appropriate knowledge, skills, and qualities (group level), and determining whether there are appropriate resources to maintain the program long term without relying on federal, state, or local grant funding (community level).

KEY STEPS OF A NEEDS ASSESSMENT[1]

— A needs assessment often includes examining both quantitative and qualitative data. These data can be used to better understand the expressed and observed needs for a health education program. Conducting a needs assessment requires the health educator to follow a process that engages multiple stakeholders and a variety of data collection sources and methods. These data will help to validate the need before beginning to plan the health education program. The key steps are:

1. Determine the purpose of the needs assessment.
2. Identify available data to assess the health problem.
3. Decide on the data collection approach and gather data.
4. Analyze and interpret the data.
5. Identify factors linked to the health problem(s).
6. Identify the focus of the program and begin the planning process.

DETERMINING THE PURPOSE OF THE NEEDS ASSESSMENT

— In order to effectively plan a needs assessment, it is important to understand first how it will be used and who will participate in the needs assessment process. This includes the most appropriate needs assessment strategy and having a general idea of human and financial resources available for the assessment. Defining the target population—or "who" is being assessed—is an important first step in conducting the needs assessment.
— Health educators should determine the purpose of the survey—will it be used to determine knowledge, attitudes, beliefs, behaviors, skills, and/or health status of a population?

There are three factors identified in a needs assessment (Green & Kreuter, 1992).

— 1. Predisposing Factors—Characteristics of a person or population that motivate behavior prior to or during the occurrence of that behavior. They include knowledge, beliefs, values, and attitudes.

---

[1]   NCHEC Competency 1.1. Plan assessment process for health education/promotion.

2. Enabling Factors—Internal and external conditions directly related to the issues that help people adopt and maintain healthy or unhealthy behaviors and lifestyles, or to embrace or reject particular environmental conditions. These include available resources, services, laws/policies, and skill sets.

3. Reinforcing Factors—Attitudes that support or make it difficult to adopt healthy behaviors or foster healthy environments. This includes the influence of family members, peers, teachers, employers, health providers, the media, community leaders, politicians, and other decision makers.

It is also important to establish a set of parameters that can be used to conduct the needs assessment. Health educators should consider utilizing a model to guide the needs assessment, such as the Epidemiological Model, Public Health Model, Social Model, Asset Model, Precede–Proceed Model (see Chapter 3), or the Rapid Model (Issel, 2004).

The Epidemiological Model for needs assessments focuses on determining health problems for a given target population by measuring objectively those problems that pose the greatest threat to health and quality of life. This includes studying the distribution and determinants of health problems or events in terms of the population. Key questions include:

- What is the problem?
- Who has the problem?
- Why do those with the problem have it?

The Public Health Model is similar to the Epidemiological Model. It focuses on quantifying health problems through existing and epidemiological data, but tends to focus on a specific population and is a valuable model when there are resource limitations. Two commonly used examples of this model are the Planned Approach to Community Health (PATCH) and Mobilizing for Action through Planning and Partnership (MAPP). Both focus on identifying assets and needs by utilizing community engagement to plan, conduct, and evaluate health promotion and disease prevention programs (CDC, 2014).

The Social Model for needs assessment focuses on identifying the social, economic, and political issues that can influence health (Issel, 2004). The model focuses more on societal trends than other models do, and relies on collecting data on social indicators such as income, social norms, and other social resources. Potential sources of social indicator data come from the U.S. Census Surveys (U.S. Census Bureau, 2015), including the American

Community Survey (ACS), the American Housing Survey (AHS), the Current Population Survey (CPS), the Consumer Expenditure (CE) Survey, and the National Health Interview Survey (NHIS).

– Another model for conducting needs assessments focuses more on community strengths. The Asset Model examines the existing assets of a community, organization, or population that can help to improve health. An assets-based assessment focuses specifically identifying community resources, creating or strengthening relationships between community members and organizations, mobilizing the community around its resources, rallying the community to develop a health vision for the future, and introducing outside resources to fill identified gaps. Thus, this model focuses on the potential social capital of a community or group given a particular health problem, as well as on community competence—a community's ability to identify health problems and take action to address them. Two commonly used models for addressing a community's strengths are Kretzmann and McKnight's (1996) Asset-Based Community Development (ABCD) and the Asset Model (AM), which focus on greater participation of local communities to assess health problems (Morgan & Ziglio, 2007).

– The Rapid Model is a tool for conducting needs assessments when there is limited time, an in-depth assessment is not practical, or an impending crisis requires immediate action. The purpose of a rapid needs assessment for health educators is to collect information quickly, especially when time and money are limited. It may involve multiple methods, such as using brief interviews, focus groups, and existing data from the involved community to rapidly develop and implement health interventions. Two commonly used rapid-assessment models are Rapid Assessment and Response (RAR) and Rapid Assessment, Response and Evaluation (RARE). Both models focus on an assessment of complex health issues and behaviors within a short time frame, and offer a means for responding quickly with appropriate health education program measures and interventions (Issel, 2004; Trotter, Needle, Goosby, Bates, & Singer, 2001).

IDENTIFYING AVAILABLE DATA TO ASSESS THE HEALTH PROBLEM[2]

– It is important to locate existing data as well as to plan for collecting new data. There may also be useful secondary data that have already been collected, which can help to save time, money, and other resources. It is

---

[2] NCHEC Competency 1.2. Access existing information and data related to health.

important to conduct a thorough review of the available data. Often, other public health agencies or community organizations are already conducting or planning to conduct a needs assessment. There are generally three sources of data:

1. Primary data collection involves original or new data.

2. Secondary data are those collected by others, and are often readily available and inexpensive to obtain. Potential sources of secondary data include federal, state, and local health departments; federally qualified health centers; hospitals; and other health organizations. Secondary data may also include information on mortality and morbidity, such as rates of disease, injury, and disability; sources for these type of data may include *The Morbidity and Mortality Weekly Report* (*MMWR*), published by the CDC, as well as data from peer-reviewed health and medical journals.

3. Tertiary data may be found in publications such as encyclopedias, pamphlets, fact sheets, and other reference tools that sum up primary and secondary sources.

DECIDE ON THE DATA COLLECTION APPROACH AND GATHER DATA[3]

After a review of existing data, health educators play an important role in determining additional data collection approaches that will be needed to gather other valuable data. It is important to consider the best data collection methods that will be useful and fit within the predetermined timeline. Health educators should collect data by using the most appropriate research methods. There are several key issues to consider when collecting data for a needs assessment: the data needed, data collection methods, sampling techniques, research design, and the validity and reliability of instruments.

The data needed for the needs assessment should tie back to the purpose of the needs assessment, including the target population and available resources for the needs assessment. Due to the limited resources for data collection, it is often important to collect only the minimum amount of data necessary to address the needs of the target population.

The data collection methods chosen for a needs assessment can affect how the information can be used. It may be important to collect data from

---

[3] NCHEC Competency 1.3. Collect primary data to determine needs.

different sources, including archival data (medical or agency records); public data (CDC or other national data sources); primary data sources (surveys, interviews, observations, community forums, focus groups, nominal group processes, Delphi panels, self-assessment instruments, and community-capacity data); observational data (environmental scans of health behaviors such as public smoking- or tobacco-related advertisements in convenience stores); published literature (literature reviews or summaries of other published works); and other sources (community stakeholder input, local news, and social media).

PRIMARY DATA COLLECTION METHODS—QUALITATIVE

Qualitative research is a broad methodological approach that seeks to understand a situation by exploring the perspectives of those involved in the situation. Qualitative researchers use a variety of methods, including qualitative methods, to gain understanding. In this section, we review four of these methods commonly used in health education.

What Is a Focus Group?

A focus group is a qualitative method in which, generally, six to 10 individuals are invited to participate in a group interview about their perceptions, opinions, beliefs, and/or attitudes toward a specific health concern or issue. The discussion is led by a moderator, whose job is to pose questions and probe from a guide developed a priori to ensure the discussion covers the desired topics within the allotted time frame, remains fair, and ensures that all participants are encouraged to share their perspectives. Focus groups are often designed to be homogeneous around a characteristic of interest—particularly if a topic is sensitive (related to race, gender, religion, age, politics, or difficult topics such as violence), so that participants feel comfortable sharing information and there are common frames of references and/or experiences are possible.

What Is a Key Informant Interview?

Key informant interviews are also hosted by an interviewer, but generally the participants are interviewed one or two at time. This allows for more in-depth probing of the participant's views than what is possible in a focus group. Such interviews can be appropriate to gain knowledge from people with particular insight into a topic. Key informant interviews may also be more appropriate for very sensitive topics where people might not be willing to share information in a group setting, as the interviewer can get to know the participant better and develop a closer rapport than may be possible in a group setting. The downside of the method is that it is very time consuming to collect and analyze individual data.

What Is a Nominal Group Process?

In a nominal group process, a small group of individuals respond to questions, discuss answers, and then privately rank the importance of health concerns or issues. The individual rankings are then shared with group and tallied by the moderator. This process is repeated as necessary to achieve group consensus. Advantages of the nominal group process are that it is a very democratic way of making decisions and that it works well to ensure that everyone has a say in the decision, which can neutralize the effect of very dominant persons in a group. Disadvantages of the method are that it requires some preparation, takes some time, and is fairly regimented, which can lead to decisions made on less-than-developed ideas.

What Is a Delphi Panel Process?

A Delphi Panel process is used when there is no clear evidence upon which to base decisions, and thus takes advantage of the wisdom of experts to make decisions or recommendations (Bensley & Brookins-Fisher, 2009). They generate consensus through use of structure questionnaires, generally distributed among experts or thought leaders on a given topic. The questionnaires are revised each time (a range of three to five times per session) and sent back to participants to achieve consensus.

Triangulation means exploring multiple points of view, angles, and perspective in a given setting, and establishing "dialogue" among these perspectives, as well as integrating them into the analysis of findings. In a broader research context, triangulation may also involve employing multiple and differing methodological approaches and methodologies, different sources of information, and differing theoretical perspectives in order to study a given question or setting. These approaches, instruments, sources, perspectives, and so on—despite the name—do not need to number three.

PRIMARY DATA COLLECTION METHODS–QUANTITATIVE

Survey Research Method

Surveys are one of the most popular tools for conducting primary data collection. They are relatively inexpensive to develop, distribute, and analyze. Depending on your population and topic of interest, substantial amounts of data can be developed from surveys to inform research and programmatic choices. No wonder they are so frequently used by health educators to assess needs and to plan and evaluate programs! However, there are some limitations to keep in mind: Surveys can have very low response rates, especially without incentives, and can be, depending on the population of interest, difficult to get into the hands of the people you are most interested in hearing from. This is especially true for vulnerable populations, such as the homeless, those who cannot read, displaced populations, the very young, and the very old. Still, surveys remain a critical tool for a health educator.

There are several stepsto consider when developing a survey:

1. It is important to plan the survey by determining objectives and resources.
2. The health educator must design the survey in order to meet the objectives within the scope of the available resources.
3. It is important to collect data in the way that ensures that the objectives will be achieved in line with the available resources.
4. It is important to plan for the data analysis and ensure that the goals and objectives of the needs assessment are met.

Choosing an appropriate research design is important for health educators who are collecting primary data. Typically, health educators will use observational designs to better understand how various factors may results in a health problem or condition. Observational designs include **cross-sectional** (one-time data collection; present or recall of past); group comparisons, including **case-control** (which matches an intervention participant with a control participant; present and recall of past); and **longitudinal** (prospective, and includes present and future data) designs.

Experimental designs include both present and past data, but participants are randomly assigned to either the experimental or control group. Experimental designs are usually not appropriate for needs assessments, but should be considered if the data could be used during the program evaluation stage.

Barriers to using experimental designs include their expense and reliance on a control group (individual or community) to compare the effects of a health intervention. Also, the control group needs to be equivalent to the experimental group.

For nonexperimental designs, there are various sampling techniques, such as convenience or snowball sampling. The drawing on the sample will depend on the accessibility of the target population and the sample size needed.

When constructing a survey or choosing existing data collection tools, it is also important to consider both the validity and reliability of the tools.

Validity refers to the degree the instrument measures what it is intended to measure.

Reliability is concerned with the degree to which the instrument yields the same results each time it is used as well as when it is used with different populations.

When constructing a new survey, it is important to pretest it with a group or population that is similar to the target populations for the needs assessment. Based on the pretest results, it may be necessary to further revise the survey in order to better measure the key objectives.

ANALYZE AND INTERPRET THE DATA

Health educators need to rely on data analysts and others who can aid in turning raw data into useful information. They also need to provide answers to questions being asked at a health education program and about outcomes (Harris, 2010). Remember that even the greatest amount of and best-quality data will mean nothing if they are not properly analyzed or not analyzed at all.

Data analysis does not necessarily mean using complicated data analysis software. It just may involve looking at the data you collected and determining whether they can help you to answer the questions you need to answer. For example, if you need to know whether your health education program is meeting its objectives you can look at your program targets and compare them to the actual program performance.

There are seven steps in analyzing survey data:

1. Administer the survey: the method should fit with objectives.
2. Prepare data: code questions and answers, limit data entry errors.
3. Verify data: test for accuracy or coding errors.

4. Enter the data.

5. Tabulate the data.

6. Analyze the data.

7. Record and report the data, which should include objectives, hypothesis, a description of the survey steps, and the reliability of results.

One form of analysis, called descriptive analysis, describes the sample or target populations (Harris, 2010). It does not define causality. An example of this would be the average number of clients seen per month. Additional examples of descriptive analysis include:

Rates—measures in respect to another measures' quantity over the same time period.

Mean—average score, or the values obtained by dividing the sum of a set of quantities by the number of quantities in the set.

Median—the middle of a distribution of a set of values.

Similar to analyzing data, a health educator needs to know how to make use of needs assessment data. Following is a list of steps in analyzing assessment findings (McKenzie, Neiger, & Thackeray, 2016):

1. Analyze the data.

2. Compare them with local, state, or national data.

3. Consider the social, cultural, and political environment.

4. Set priorities:

   a. Asses the size and scope of the problem.

   b. Determine the effectiveness of possible interventions.

   c. Determine the appropriateness, economics, acceptability, resources, and legality of interventions.

For intervention mapping, there are five steps to consider (Bartholomew, Parcel, & Kok, 1998):

1. Create a matrix of the immediate program objectives.

2. Select a theory- or evidence-based intervention with appropriate methods and strategies.

3. Design and organize the intervention.

4. Specify the implementation plans.

5. Generate the program evaluation plans.

Primary, Secondary, and Tertiary Prevention

Primary prevention involves delaying or preventing illness or injury (Gordon, 1983; World Health Organization, 2017).

Examples

Implementing a routine immunization program for children.

Eliminating environmental risks, such as contaminated water.

Enhancing the nutritional status of low-income mothers.

Secondary prevention involves an effort to diagnosis an illness or injury early and/or encourage early treatment.

Examples

Routine screening for major forms of cancer.

Early detection of risk for falls among older adults.

Conducting health screening for inner-city youth at risk for type 2 diabetes.

Tertiary prevention focuses on providing treatment and recovery from an illness or injury.

Examples

Increasing access to affordable treatments for individuals with early-stage cancers.

Providing medicines, such as inhalers and bronchodilators, to steelworkers at risk for asthma.

Offering free outpatient treatment for individuals with hypertension.

Considering the Relationship Among Behavioral, Environmental, Policy, and Other Factors That Influence Health[4]

In the needs assessment phase, it is important to consider different kinds of factors that can influence health. There are a number of ways to do this, including considering the social determinants of health and the social-ecological model. According to *Healthy People 2020* (U.S. Department of Health and Human Services, 2014), the social determinants of health "are conditions in the environments in which people are born, live, learn, work, play, worship, and age that affect a wide range of health, functioning, and quality-of-life outcomes and risks," and includes economic stability, neighborhood and built environment, health and healthcare, social and community context, and education. The social-ecological model is a systems model that surrounds the individual with multiple bands of influence, radiating out from the individual through the interpersonal to institutions, the community, and, finally, to public policy and laws. At the needs assessment level, health educators should consider which factors—biological, behavioral, environmental, policy, and so on—are involved in creating the health problem being addressed.

Barriers to and Facilitators of Health Education

Health promotion and education often focuses on behaviors or risk factors rather than identifying the range of factors that affect the health behaviors (Robinson, Driedger, Elliott, & Eyles, 2006). For more information on facilitating adult learning, see Chapter 7. For information on writing learning objectives, including Bloom's Taxonomy, see Chapter 3.

Interpersonal health behaviors are typically the product of interaction between individual and environmental factors (Glanz, Rimer, & Viswanath, 2008). In order to drive behavior change, individuals need to develop supportive beliefs, training, and/or skills and they may need incentives and/or reinforcements; the social and physical environment also needs to support the behavior change.

As mentioned earlier, facilitators of and barriers to a health education program may include attitudes, or predisposing factors, and the necessary

---

[4] NCHEC Competency 1.4. Analyze relationships among behavioral, environmental, and other factors that influence health.

action, skills, and resources that enable behavior change and feedback, or reinforcing factors (Green & Kreuter, 1992).

Socioecological theory holds that the interconnections between groups and organizations and the broader environmental context may also influence health promotion and education efforts positively or negatively (Robinson et al., 2006).

Potential Barriers to Health Education

Health literacy (poor communication)

Competing priorities or lack of interest

Lack of skilled and/or committee people

Lack of funds and resources

Lack of leadership

Unsupportive environment

Transportation or geographic challenges

Lack of time

Weak partnerships

Potential Facilitators of Health Education

Strong partnerships

Sustaining structure/coordination

Evidence that the health education/promotion program works

Adaptability to needs

Good communication

Funds and resources

Low response burden

Bringing it All Together[5]

Once you have conducted and analyzed your needs assessment, your work is not quite finished. Your last step should be to return to your

---

[5] NCHEC Competency 1.5. Examine factors that influence the process by which people learn; NCHEC Competency 1.6. Examine factors that influence the process of health education/promotion; NCHEC Competency 1.7. Determine needs for health education/promotion based on assessment findings.

populations and validate what you think you have found with them to make sure you have heard what they have said. Just as you likely used multiple methods to uncover needs in the population, you will likely use multiple methods to "check back" with them to synthesize and prioritize needs. You will have to decide which needs are more and less changeable and which are of greater and lesser importance. This will help you as you move into the next phase, program planning. Often, needs assessment ends with some kind of reporting process, which can be formal or informal. Consider reporting in a variety of formats as appropriate to your audience, including written reports, in-person presentations, online and/or social media posts, and infographics. And remember to make reports accessible in terms of reading levels, languages, and disabilities.

CONCLUSION

Needs assessment is a critical first step in developing health education programs and materials that will have the maximum positive effect and avoid wasting time and resources or creating unintended consequences. It can be thought of as the foundation on which you build your health education house—a weak foundation will lead to building problems down the line. In Chapter 3, we will review how to apply the results of the needs assessment to the next step in the process—planning for health education/promotion, which is Area II.

REVIEW QUESTIONS:

1. Which statement is NOT true about participant observation?

   A. It can provide guidance on sampling interviewees.
   B. It includes informal interviews in the field.
   C. It yields best results when it is covert.
   D. It aims for understanding of the setting's culture cognitively and by "feeling" it.

2. Which statement is true about interviewers during qualitative, in-depth interviews?

   A. They try to avoid using probes or follow-up questions.
   B. They read each question exactly as it appears on the interview questionnaire.

- C. They need to convey genuine interest in the interviewee's responses.
  D. They agree with the participant's responses and take their side to build rapport.

3. Which statement is a good recommendation about field notes?

   A. If the budget permits, substitute audio or video recording for written notes.
   B. Write down the main events and ignore small talk and routine information.
   C. Reread notes often, and record any ideas that come to you during the process of rereading.
   - D. To maintain objectivity, write about what happened in the field and what others said, but avoid writing about how you felt.

4. Which statement is true about selection in qualitative research?

   A. A researcher does not need to write a strategy for selecting cases in the research proposal. The best strategy will become apparent as the research proceeds.
   B. Participants can help recruit other participants.
   C. In selecting participants, a researcher should strive for maximum variation.
   - D. If possible, random sampling is the gold standard.

5. Which statement is NOT true about someone who uses qualitative research methods?

   A. They often assume an identity other than their own.
   B. They use rigorous, systematic methods.
   C. They usually need to interact with people in the setting to gain access.
   D. They can change the data collection strategy if the initial data suggest this is necessary.

6. Which of these ethical considerations does NOT apply to participant observation?

   A. Not harming the participants
   B. Ensuring the participants' privacy
   C. Ensuring that all participants provide written, informed consent
   - D. Being respectful of cultural differences

7. Coding is a qualitative analytic technique used to:

   A. Eliminate unimportant data
   B. Sort and categorize themes and concepts by labeling them
   C. Create comprehensive lists of corresponding symbols
   D. Coordinate triangulation among different theories

8. If a respondent does NOT understand the question during a telephone survey, the interviewer should:

   A. Rephrase the question in local terms, based on familiarity with the area.
   - B. Read the question again or clarify the text in the survey.
   C. Go to the next question.
   D. Try to guess the best answer, given the respondent's characteristics.

9. Closed-ended questions:

   A. Are not popular in survey research
   - B. Are easier to recode and analyze
   C. Encourage the respondent to elaborate on responses
   D. Should have a few, general response categories

10. What is the major weakness of this survey item?

    "How old were you when your parents first took you to a restaurant?"

    i. *Under 6 months old*
    ii. *6 to 12 months old*
    iii. *13 to 24 months old*
    iv. *25 months to 3 years old*
    v. *Older than age 3*
    vi. *They never took me to a restaurant*

    A. It is double barreled
    B. It is not mutually exclusive
    C. Respondents are not fully capable of answering
    D. It uses jargon

Use Figure 2.1 for questions 11 and 12

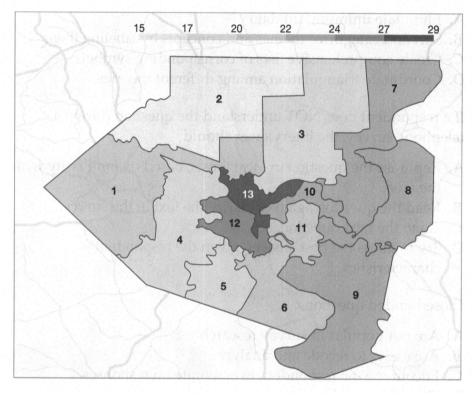

Figure 2.1 County prevalence of depression by district.

11. A health educator is presented with data on the lifetime prevalence of depression by district within this county. Which of the following can be said?

    A. The prevalence of depression ranges from 1% to 13%.
    – **B.** Districts 12 and 13 have the highest rates of depression.
    C. District 11 has higher rates of depression than District 5.
    D. Living on the east side of the county reduces the likelihood of experiencing depression.

12. After reviewing the data in Figure 2.1, the health educator is concerned about rates of depression in several districts within the county. Which of the following would be a primary source of data for a needs assessment?

    A. Published data from the county health department
    B. Review of hospital admissions for suicide attempts
    – **C.** Interviews with crisis response workers
    D. Review of claims paid by insurance companies for depression-related treatments

13. What is NOT true of a good health-related research question?

   A. It can be answered empirically.
   B. It identifies a topic but never a specific population.
   C. It can be written as a question.
   D. It is ethical.

14. "Colorectal cancer among African American men in Alabama"

   A. Is not a good research question because the population is too specific
   B. Is a topic, not a question
   C. Can be a good research question if reworded as: "How can we eliminate the problem of colorectal cancer among African American men in Alabama?"
   D. Can be a good research question if reworded as: "What are the evidence-based interventions to detect colorectal cancer among African American men?"

15. Lack of flexibility, high likelihood of unanswered questions, a low response rate, and the inability to record extraneous reactions or comments are all limitations of what kinds of survey techniques?

   A. Mail
   B. Telephone
   C. Face-to-face
   D. Web-based

16. The best data for understanding the needs of your audience generally come from:

   A. A large investment in primary research
   B. A combination of secondary sources and qualitative and quantitative primary research
   C. Extensive use of focus groups and in-depth interviews to gain rich, deep data about the audience and their needs
   D. An exhaustive review of the literature

17. "The population in County A experiences larger morbidity rates for several diseases than County B. Both counties have similar per capita income. Therefore, the health differences must be caused by something other than income level." This is an example of

   A. Tautology
   B. Reductionism
   C. Ecological fallacy
   D. Spuriousness

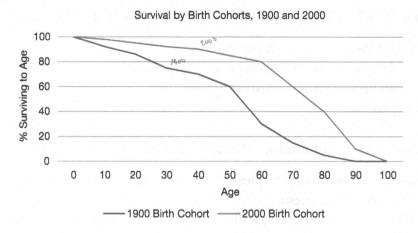

Figure 2.2 Survival by birth cohorts, 1900 and 2000.

18. Figure 2.2 shows the proportion of two birth cohorts, one born in 1900 and one in 2000, surviving to old age. For example, 100% are alive at birth, age 0, for both cohorts, but the mortality experience for each is quite different. Looking at the survival plots, which is not true?

   A. Life expectancy has increased.
   B. Median survival increased by about 20 years.
   C. The 1900 birth cohort had the highest mortality rate between the ages 50 and 60.
   D. No one born in 1900 reached age 85 or greater.

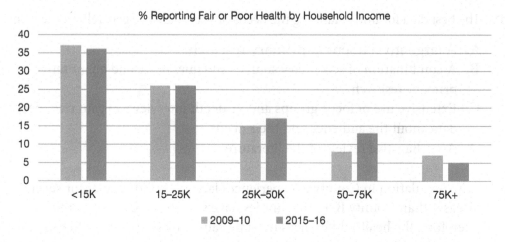

Figure 2.3 Percentage reporting fair or poor health by household income.

19. What conclusions can you draw from Figure 2.3?

    A. Health disparities based on income are declining.

    B. The prevalence of fair or poor health is increasing.

  – **C.** The odds of reporting fair or poor health are about six to seven times higher in people earning less than $15K compared to people earning $75K.

    D. The odds of reporting fair or poor health are about three times lower in people earning $15K to $25K compared to people earning less than 15K.

20. The following correctly describes triangulation, except that:

  – **A.** Triangulation means using three approaches in studying a topic or setting.

    B. Triangulation involves comparing different sources and points of observation.

    C. Triangulation may help contextualize data gathered.

    D. Triangulation may involve using more than one method of data gathering.

ANSWERS

1. A. It can provide guidance on sampling interviewees

Participant observation includes developing rapport; taking extensive, reflexive field notes; and, in many cases, interviews. Because it is an immersive technique, you would not set up a purposive sampling technique.

2. D. They agree with the participant's responses and take their side to build rapport

While remaining pleasant, a good interviewer builds rapport, asks questions, uses probes, and conveys interests in the interviewee while remaining neutral during an interview.

3. C. Reread notes often, and record any ideas that come to you during the process of rereading

Adding audio/video recording as an addition to (but not replacement for) field notes is a great way to collect more data in the field and can yield additional data. But field notes must be read, and reread, often and the researcher must be constantly thinking about and noting ideas and themes that arise during the collection of data.

4. B. Participants can help recruit other participants

Unlike in quantitative data collection, you can often use participants in qualitative data collection to help identify and recruit appropriate participants for qualitative data through snowball sampling.

5. A. They often assume an identity other than their own

In general, when using qualitative methods, we do not change our identity. In fact, the principles of informed consent nearly always dictate that we fully disclose who we are as researchers and what we are doing in a particular study.

6. C. Ensuring that all participants provide written, informed consent

By nature, it is impossible to provide written (or even verbal), informed consent when conducting a participant observation study, since the researcher is unobtrusively observing the behavior of the participants.

7. B. Sort and categorize themes and concepts by labeling them

Qualitative data is coded or sorted and categorized into themes and concepts by labeling them in ways that make sense to the researchers who are trying to answer questions about the participants.

8. B. Read the question again or clarify the text in the survey

When administering a telephone survey, it is important to stick to the written script of materials. Rereading questions and clarifying text is fine; rephrasing material or guessing a participant's responses is not.

9. B. Are easier to recode and analyze

One of the advantages of using closed-ended questions in survey research is that they are easy to analyze, which is one of the reasons why they are so popular. A disadvantage is that they do not elicit further information from respondents.

10. C. Respondents are not fully capable of answering

Respondents would not be able to remember when they were that young, and so would not be able to answer the question appropriately.

11. B. Districts 12 and 13 have the highest rates of depression

The map shows that Districts 12 and 13 have the highest rates of depression. Prevalence ranges from 15% to 29%, and District 5 has a higher rate than District 11. While rates vary across the county, generally rates on the east side of the county are higher than rates on the west side.

12. C. Interviews with crisis response workers

Interviews conducted by the health educator would be considered primary data collection—the others are reviewing data collected by others (health departments, hospitals, health insurance companies).

13. B. Identifies a topic but never a specific population

Health-related research questions nearly always are related to specific populations.

14. B. Is a topic, not a question

Colorectal cancer among African American men in Alabama is a topic, not a question. Neither of the research questions listed are workable—the first, because it is highly unlikely that colorectal cancer could ever be eliminated because it has multiple determinates, all of which would need to be addressed differently. The second, "What are the evidence-based interventions to detect colorectal cancer?" is not a research question—that information exists and is discoverable through a literature search.

15. A. Mail

Mail-based surveys can eliminate interviewer bias, are relatively inexpensive to distribute, and promote interrater reliability (to name a few of their advantages), but suffer from some serious limitations as well. Telephone (especially when computer assisted) and web-based surveys allow for more flexibility with complex skip patterns and reduce the likelihood of unanswered questions. Face-to-face interviews also reduce the likelihood of unanswered questions and allow for the recording of spontaneous and/or nonverbal reactions.

16. B. A combination of secondary sources and qualitative and quantitative primary research

The combination of secondary sources, which can tell you what has been tried in the past, what has been successful, and what has not, provide you with vital statistics, demographics, and so on. And a mixed-methods primary research strategy, which can provide specific generalizable data as well as rich, deep qualitative data, is most likely to provide a health educator with the best information from which to plan a program.

A great place to start a new program is to identify community gatekeepers and determine the needs and concerns of the community. Not only will the health department staff learn what people already know about lead in their community, but they will also get valuable insight into the cultures of the community. It will be critical for health department staff to ask local gatekeepers what other gatekeepers they should be talking to make sure that they have hear from representatives from the whole community if the immigrants come from many different places. Good places to start may be community centers, places of worship, and social service agencies.

17. C. Ecological fallacy

Ecological fallacy is an error made in reasoning about differing units of analysis. Specifically, it is an error of using data generated from groups as the unit of analysis and attempting to draw conclusions about individuals. Per capita income is a summary measure at the level of the county (which is the unit of analysis). We do not have any information about the distribution of income among individuals. Therefore, we do not know if income was related to the health outcomes, which is a different unit of analysis (the individual level).

18. D. No one born in 1900 reached age 85 or greater

The 2000 birth curve consistently shifts to the right, indicating that life expectancy and survival has increased. The 1900 cohort had 30 people die in their 50s—nearly a third of the cohort. For those in the 1900 cohort, we know that five of them entered the cohort at 80 and all were dead by 90, but we do not know when they died. The graph shows a decline over the decade, but cannot tell us exactly when they died.

19. C. The odds of reporting fair or poor health are about six to seven times higher in people earning less than $15K compared to people earning $75K

Lower income is strongly associated with reporting poorer health.

20. A. Triangulation means using three approaches in studying a topic or setting

Triangulation means exploring multiple points of view, angles, and perspectives in a given setting, establishing "dialogue" among these perspectives, and integrating them into the analysis of findings. In a broader research context. Triangulation may also involve employing multiple and differing methodological approaches and methodologies, different sources of information, and differing theoretical perspectives in order to study a given question or setting. These approaches, instruments, sources, perspectives, and so on, despite the name, do not need to number three.

REFERENCES

Aday, L. A., & Cornelius, L. J. (2011). *Designing and conducting health surveys: A comprehensive guide.* Hoboken, NJ: John Wiley & Sons.

Bartholomew, L. K., Parcel, G. S., & Kok, G. (1998). Intervention mapping: A process for developing theory and evidence-based health education programs. *Health Education & Behavior, 25*(5), 545–563. doi:10.1177/109019819802500502

Bensley, R. J., & Brookins-Fisher, J. (Eds.). (2009). *Community health education methods: A practical guide* (3rd ed.). Sudbury, MA: Jones and Bartlett.

Centers for Disease Control and Prevention. (2014). *Assessment & planning models, frameworks & tools.* Retrieved from http://www.cdc.gov/stltpublichealth/cha/assessment.html

Centers for Disease Control and Prevention. (2015). Physical activity: Needs assessment. Retrieved from https://www.cdc.gov/physicalactivity/worksite-pa/toolkits/fitnessclub/needsassessment101.htm

Centers for Disease Control and Prevention. (2017). National Diabetes Prevention Program: Implement a lifestyle change program for professionals. Retrieved from https://www.cdc.gov/diabetes/prevention/lifestyle-program/index.html

Gilmore, G. D. (2012). *Needs and capacity assessment strategies for health promotion and health education* (4th ed.). Sudbury, MA: Jones and Bartlett.

Glanz, K., Rimer, B. K., & Viswanath, K. (Eds.). (2008). *Health behavior and health education: Theory, research, and practice.* Hoboken, NJ: John Wiley & Sons.

Gordon, R. S., Jr. (1983). An operational classification of disease prevention. *Public Health Reports, 98*(2), 107–109. doi:10.1037/e659532007-006

Green, L. W., & Kreuter, M. W. (1992). CDC's planned approach to community health as an application of PRECEDE and an inspiration for PROCEED. *Journal of Health Education, 23,* 140–147. doi:10.1080/10556699.1992.10616277

Harris, M. (2010). *Evaluating public and community health programs.* San Francisco, CA: Jossey-Bass.

Issel, L. M. (2004). *Health program planning and evaluation: A practical, systematic approach for community health.* Sudbury, MA: Jones and Bartlett.

Kretzmann, J., & McKnight, J. P. (1996). Assets-based community development. *National Civic Review, 85,* 23–13. doi:10.1002/ncr.4100850405

McKenzie, J. F., Neiger, B. L., & Thackeray, R. (2016). *Planning, implementing & evaluating health promotion programs: A primer.* New York, NY: Pearson.

Morgan, A., & Ziglio, E. (2007). Revitalising the evidence base for public health: An assets model. *Promotion & Education, 14*(Suppl. 2), 17–22. doi:10.1177/10253823070140020701x

Robinson, K. L., Driedger, M. S., Elliott, S. J., & Eyles, J. (2006). Understanding facilitators of and barriers to health promotion practice. *Health Promotion Practice, 7*(4), 467–476. doi:10.1177/1524839905278955

Trotter, R. T., Needle, R. H., Goosby, E., Bates, C., & Singer, M. (2001). A methodological model for rapid assessment, response, and evaluation: The RARE program in public health. *Field Methods, 13*(2), 137–159. doi:10.1177/1525822x0101300202

U.S. Census Bureau (2015). *List of household surveys.* Retrieved from http://www.census.gov/programs-surveys/are-you-in-a-survey/survey-list/household-survey-list.html

U.S. Department of Health and Human Services. (2014). *Healthy people 2020.* Retrieved from https://www.healthypeople.gov/2020/topics-objectives/topic/social-determinants-of-health

World Health Organization. (2017). *EPHO5: Disease prevention, including early detection of illness.* Retrieved from http://www.euro.who.int/en/health-topics/Health-systems/public-health-services/policy/the-10-essential-public-health-operations/epho5-disease-prevention,-including-early-detection-of-illness2

Chapter 3

Area II: Plan Health Education/Promotion

INTRODUCTION

This chapter covers how to plan health education and promotion programs. Health education specialists utilize skills every day that help with the planning, implementation, and evaluation of programs. This chapter focuses on planning of health education programs and interventions. It includes an overview of how to identify priority populations, how to develop goals and objectives, strategies for selecting or designing effective strategies and/or interventions, how to develop the plan for implementation and delivery, and the need for identifying and addressing both facilitators of and barriers to implementation.

USE STRATEGIES TO IDENTIFY PRIORITY HEALTH PROBLEMS IN ORDER TO PLAN FOR HEALTH EDUCATION AND PROMOTION[1]

It may seem overwhelming at first when you are trying to identify the most useful strategies for planning health education and promotion programs and interventions. It will be helpful to consider a model or theory to guide you in program planning and development, especially when trying to create or modify strategies that will lead to an evidence-based program and intervention.

---

[1] NCHEC Competency 2.4. Develop a plan for the delivery of health education/promotion; NCHEC Competency 2.5. Address factors that influence the implementation of health education/promotion.

Theories and models provide a road map and strategies for identifying health problems, developing appropriate interventions, and evaluating the successes of the interventions. They can inform the planner's thinking during all of these stages, offering insights that translate into stronger programs. Theory can also help to explain the dynamics of health behaviors, including processes for changing them, and the influences of the many forces that affect health behaviors, including social and physical environments. Theory can also help planners identify the most suitable target audiences, methods for fostering change, and outcomes for evaluation.

Theories Versus Models

Theory: A set of interrelated constructs, definitions, and statements that present a systematic view of events or situations by specifying the relationships among variables, with the sole purpose of explaining and predicting the events or situations.

Model: A system that often draws upon several theories to better understand a health problem in a specific setting or context.

Source: Glanz, K., Rimer, B. K., and Viswanath, K. (Eds.). (2008). *Health behavior and health education: Theory, research, and practice* (4th ed.). San Francisco, CA: Jossey-Bass.

PRECEDE–PROCEED MODEL

The PRECEDE–PROCEED model is a community-oriented, participatory model aimed at developing successful community health education and promotion programs and interventions (Glanz & Rimer, 2005).

PRECEDE–PROCEED Model

The Five Phases of the PRECEDE Model:

Phase 1: Social diagnosis

Phase 2: Epidemiological diagnosis

Phase 3: Behavioral and environmental diagnosis

Phase 4: Educational and organizational diagnosis

Phase 5: Administrative and policy diagnosis

(continued)

(*continued*)

The Four Phases of the PROCEED Model:

Phase 6: Implementation

Phase 7: Process evaluation

Phase 8: Impact evaluation

Phase 9: Outcome evaluation

The PRECEDE–PROCEED model is a logic model to guide you in the planning process, and it provides some structure for you and your stakeholders for developing a health education program and/or intervention. The PRECEDE–PROCEED model also highlights the importance of participatory approaches and how to ensure community and stakeholder involvement (Glanz & Rimer, 2005).

PRECEDE–PROCEED incorporates a multilevel evaluation, which we will be discussing in **Chapter 5**. It includes processes for monitoring and adjusting your evaluation approach. Since the model focuses on program planning, it also provides some flexibility and allows for the adaptation of content and methods that are most relevant to your program/intervention and the particular needs and circumstances of your community and stakeholders.

PRECEDE stands for Predisposing, Reinforcing, Enabling Constructs in Educational/Environmental Diagnosis and Evaluation. **Predisposing factors**, such as knowledge, attitudes, beliefs, values, or other factors, may motivate or be responsible for a given behavior and may impact readiness to change. This also includes identifying potential barriers to health education programs. **Enabling factors** include those influences that enable an individual to act on a specific behavior, such as resources, services, supportive policies, and other facilitators of health education programs. **Reinforcing factors** are influences that encourage repeated behaviors or incentivize continued practice of the behavior, such as social support, rewards, praise, or symptom relief.

Phase 1: Social diagnosis—Multiple sources of data collection that focus on better understanding the perceived needs of a community (i.e., focus groups, key informant interviews, surveys, and participant observation).

Phase 2: Epidemiological diagnosis—Typically involves secondary health outcome data or data that describe a health problem and potential causes of the health problem. These data are often used to develop program goals and objectives.

Phase 3: Behavioral and environmental diagnosis—This includes data on internal and external factors that influence behavior and the environment. Often these data may come from literature reviews or theories that can be used to explain behavior.

Phase 4: Educational and organizational diagnosis—This includes data on individual-, interpersonal-, or community-level theories that can identify and describe the key determinants of health behaviors. These areas are typically classified as predisposing, reinforcing, or enabling factors.

Phase 5: Administrative and policy diagnosis—This involves a diagnosis of strategies and data from the administrative and policy-level sources. It includes data collected from previous steps, including availability of resources and organizational policies that may impact program implementation.

PROCEED stands for Policy, Regulatory, and Organizational Constructs in Educational and Environmental Development. These steps focus on program implementation and evaluation.

Phase 6: Implementation—This phase involves processes for implementing and evaluating the health education program.

Phase 7: Process evaluation—This focuses on program fidelity or the extent to which a program is being implemented as it was designed and planned.

Phase 8: Impact evaluation—This examines changes in predisposing, enabling, and reinforcing factors and the influence of a program on the desired behavioral and environmental changes.

Phase 9: Outcome evaluation—This final phase examines whether the program has affected the desired health problem.

Program planning involves identifying the needs, priorities, potential root causes of health problems, facilitators (i.e., available and needed resources), and barriers to achieving the objectives and overall goals of the program. Prior to developing your health education and promotion programs, it is important to consider any potential barriers and facilitators that could influence the success and uptake of your health education program or intervention. Health educators may want to consider using a model to aid them in the planning process. While there are many different models out there, finding the right one may be challenge if you do not know the key elements of your program.

Remember, there may not be a perfect model for your program or planning process. Often, health educators will have to either use a model that does not align that well or they may choose to use parts of the model or a combination of several planning models to best meet the needs of their program, community, and stakeholders. This is why the first phase of the needs assessment (described in Chapter 2) is so important and can help with identifying your priorities, partners, and stakeholders.

It is important to include community members and stakeholders in your program planning, development, implementation, and evaluation. Inclusive or participatory approaches will help to ensure that the program addresses the community's concerns.

Strategy is a general approach to preventing an overall health problem. For instance, a physical activity intervention for childhood obesity might involve multiple strategies, such as teaching parents about healthy cooking and encouraging parents to incorporate physical activity into family activities.

Interventions involve a set of activities or strategies to prevent a specific health problem and address the factors that contribute to the problem. For example, a physical activity intervention might involve a school-based curriculum and social norms campaign to encourage the physical activity.

Programs involve a group of strategies or interventions to address a health problem. For example, a physical activity program for adolescents might include a school-based curriculum and a home visit to obtain support from parents.

A logic model is a flowchart that provides an organized way of understanding the key elements of a program (Wholey, Hatry, & Newcomer, 2010). Logic models include resources; inputs; activities; outputs; objectives; and short-term, intermediate, and long-term outcomes. Logic models are also helpful in identifying factors that may be outside of the health educators' and program staffs' control. Logic models are especially helpful in identifying the causal links among the key elements of the program that lead to the desired program outcomes. Logic models will be discussed more in Chapter 5.

IDENTIFY PRIORITIES OF POPULATIONS, PARTNERS, AND OTHER STAKEHOLDERS

Perhaps one of the most important steps in program planning and evaluation is to identify all community partners and stakeholders who will be involved in the program or intervention. **Stakeholders** are typically individuals or groups from a specific community or agency that share a common goal, values, or identity. Stakeholders often represent the *"who"* and *"what"* of your intervention (Wholey, Hatry, & Newcomer, 2010).[2]

A community-based organization (CBO) is a public or private non-profit organization (such as a church or health agency) that represents the needs of a community or a segment of a community. CBOs are often engaged in meeting the human, educational, environmental, or public safety needs of a community (National Network of Libraries of Medicine, 2016).

Input from community-based partners and stakeholders will be critical to developing a relevant program and having a successful program evaluation. It is also important to consider the practical and political implications of having community stakeholders involved in the planning and evaluation phases. Engaging multiple stakeholders can help to facilitate collaborative efforts among populations, partners, and other stakeholders and identify priority areas.

The focus should be on what the community needs and wants and to elicit input on the plan. Key questions should be the following:

- What outcome(s) does the community find most important?
- How can a particular health problem be reduced or improved?

It is vital that health educators ask members of the community about their perceptions of the problem and about potential causes of the problem. This is an opportunity to utilize data from the needs assessment or collect additional data on a particular health problem. This should be informed by a literature review and additional data on the health problem. In order to collect data on the particular health problem, you may choose to utilize a community survey, phone interviews, focus groups, in-depth interviews, or a landscape or environmental scan (Community Tool Box, 2016; Rowel, Moore, Nowrojee, Memiah, & Bronner, 2005).

Focus groups are small panels of eight to 10 people who are knowledgeable or can share a perspective on a specific topic or health problem (Rossi, Lipsey, & Freeman, 2004). An experienced facilitator should lead the group in a discussion in order to identify the important themes or descriptions of the panels' experiences and perspectives.

Understanding community members' opinions and utilizing the data from interviews will help clarify potential aspects of the problem that are not represented in overall demographic and health statistics (CDC,

---

[2] NCHEC Competency 2.1 Involve priority population, partners, and other stakeholders in the planning process.

2016c). This may include community members' beliefs, attitudes, and knowledge of the health problem. It can aid in identifying social norms, obtaining community buy-in, and determining the priorities of the community, and may also help identify potential ideas for the interventions.

OBTAIN COMMITMENTS TO PARTICIPATE IN HEALTH EDUCATION/PROMOTION

Building partnerships with CBOs, stakeholders, and others is a necessary approach to identifying audiences to participate in health education and promotion programs. Developing relationships that encourage community partners to participate fully in the planning, implementation, and evaluation of health education/promotion programs aids health educators in maintaining long-term partnerships, where community partners will be more engaged in your program and share their experiences and expertise. Health educators should gain and practice skills in building relationships, facilitating groups, managing conflict, and navigating political landscapes and interpersonal communication in order to work with community members and stakeholders (Warrick, Culica, Quill, Spears, & Vojvodic, 2005).

Community-based participatory research (CBPR) is a method used to bring together community members to address a particular problem. CBPR involves community members in the design, implementation, evaluation, and reporting of the results of a research project or intervention (Warrick et al., 2005). This process involves researchers as facilitators and colearners rather than experts. Health educators should consider this approach when developing community partnerships and engaging community members in the planning, implementation, and evaluation of health education and promotion programs.

DEVELOP GOALS AND OBJECTIVES[3]

Program goals and objectives help health educators achieve the desired outcomes, and can help establish criteria and standards for how you will determine whether or not these outcomes are achieved (CDC, 2016a; CDC 2016b; CDC 2016c).

---

[3] NCHEC Competency 2.2. Develop goals and objectives.

Goals are broad statements about the long-term expectations or results of a health education program or intervention (CDC, 2016b). Prior to establishing goals, it is important to specify and understand the potential causes of the health problem and target population(s) for your program.

An example of a goal: Reduce the number of students in the state ages 5 to 7 who are obese.

Objectives are statements that describe the achievable results and specify the "who," "what," "why," "when," and "how" of the change to be achieved. Objectives can be established for process or outcomes, are more specific than goals, and help identify the steps necessary to reach a determined goal. Objectives are clear, specific, realistic, and measurable statements that include one indicator with a time frame.

An example of an objective: By 2015, 50% of children ages 5 to 7 will complete a school-based curriculum on physical activity and healthy eating.

SMART objectives were established to help identify the key activities of a program or intervention. **SMART** is an acronym representing five important attributes of well-written objectives: **S**pecific, **M**easurable, **A**ttainable, **R**ealistic, and **T**ime sensitive.

- **WHAT** activities will be completed?
- **WHY** it is important to complete these activities?
- **WHO** is responsible for completing the activities?
- **WHEN** will the activities be completed?
- **HOW** will these activities be completed?

SMART Objectives

1. Specific: includes the "who," "what," and "where."
2. Measurable: "how much" change is expected.
3. Attainable: is it feasible to accomplish the desired results?
4. Realistic: considers the resources, personnel, costs, and time frame.
5. Time sensitive: represents "when" the activities will be completed.

Source: Centers for Disease Control and Prevention (2016b).

Example: By (*month/year*), (*X%*) of the target population will be able to state the guideline that adults need 30-minute physical activity most days.

There are a number of different types of objectives that could be used, based on the phase of your program, specific target population, and types of data that are being collected. Two main types of objectives are process and outcome.

Process objectives are used to monitor program implementation and provide data on how well the program is doing at reaching its target audience and intended activities.

Outcome objectives are used to monitor how well a program is doing at achieving the desired results of the program. Outcome objectives are used to describe the effect of the program on the specific health problem. Often these outcome objectives are further distinguished by identifying short-term (e.g., changes in attitudes, knowledge, and skills), intermediate (e.g., changes in behavior, norms, and policy), and long-term objectives (e.g., changes in a specific health problem).

Objectives differ from activities. **Objectives** are the clear and specific statements that describe the results that will be achieved and measure progress toward the program goals. **Activities** are the tasks or events that take place as part of a program.

Example

Activity: Educate parents on physical activity guidelines for children.

SMART short-term objective: By 2015, 75% of children ages 5 to 7 will be able to state the need for 30 minutes of physical activity every day.

Objectives may also be specific to the type of activities being implemented in a program: behavioral, environmental, learning, or administrative. Environmental objectives have to do with influences on the physical or social environment. Behavioral objectives focus on behaviors or actions that help to address the health problem and goals of the program. Learning objectives have to do with changes in knowledge necessary to reach the program goal. Finally, administrative (process) objectives involve key tasks accomplished by the program staff that are necessary for implementing the program. Examples of process objectives might include the number of trainings completed, staff trained, sites reached, or number of hours of training. Process objectives are measured throughout the life of a program and include data from logbooks, inventories, and staff reports (CDC, 2016b).

DEVELOP A VISION AND MISSION STATEMENT

Having a vision and mission statement can be used to guide your health education or promotion program. A mission statement describes the *what* and *why* of your program (Community Toolbox, 2016). Mission and vision statements are similar in that they both describe the larger picture or broad goals of your program.

Vision Statement

Vision statements represent the aspirations of your program. A vision statement should be a short phrase that describes the long-term and broad goals of your program. It should represent the governing principles of your program and the greater community or population you are targeting. It should be easily understood and communicated by others and inspire others to action.

Sample vision statements:

"Create the healthiest nation in one generation"—American Public Health Association

"A healthy world through health education"—Society for Public Health Education (SOPHE)

"Every kid healthy, active, and ready to learn"—Action for Healthy Kids

Mission Statement

Mission statements should be short (about one sentence), describing the overall outcomes your program/intervention is trying to achieve and making a broad statement about the program's key goals.

Sample mission statements:

"Serve as the national focus for developing and applying disease prevention and control, environmental health, and health promotion and health education activities designed to improve the health of the people of the United States."—CDC

"Improve the health of the public and achieve equity in health status."—American Public Health Association

"To provide global leadership to the profession of health education and health promotion and to promote the health of society."—SOPHE

"To mobilize school professionals, families, and communities to take actions that lead to healthy eating, physical activity, and healthier schools where kids thrive."—Action for Healthy Kids

SELECT OR DESIGN EFFECTIVE STRATEGIES AND/OR INTERVENTIONS[4]

Learning Strategies

Health educators are often in the position of teaching and training adults. Adult learners have distinct characteristics. First, and most important, they must be shown respect, just as you would want to be respected by someone who was teaching you something. Adult learners should be thought of as autonomous and self-directed. Introduce yourself as a facilitator, not a teacher, and involve the participants as much as possible in the design of the educational materials or training. Second, adult learners come with a lifetime of experience and knowledge that you as a teacher or trainer can use to help put your information into context. In some situations, they may know more about a certain aspect of the situation you are talking about— the neighborhood, what it is like caring for someone with a disease, the frustration of trying to get a law changed year after year. Recognize their experience and encourage participants to share their experiences with you and each other.

Adult learners usually approach a learning situation with a goal, so plan your trainings to clearly state what the goals and objectives of the trainings or educational sessions will be. (We will discuss setting learning objectives in the following section.) It is important that adult learners see how new information is relevant and practical to them, either personally or professionally.

Think for a moment about how you learn best. Do you like to learn things by reading them? Hearing them? Doing them? Most of us have a preference, but science tells us that a mix is probably the best. We retain

---

[4] NCHEC Competency 2.3. Select or design strategies/interventions; NCHEC Competency 2.4. Develop a plan for the delivery of health education/promotion.

information depending on how it is presented to us or how we interact with it. Just sitting in a lecture? You may remember only 5% of what you hear. Have to teach someone something? You will probably remember much more of the information after you teach it to someone else! Selecting the method appropriate to the material is part of the health educator's job. We do not have to know a subject in its entirety to be able to teach it to someone. Here are some of the instructional strategies to choose from:

- Lectures
- Discussions
- Role-play
- Brainstorming
- Reflective writing
- Group problem solving
- Icebreakers
- Quizzes
- Games
- Simulations
- Tabletops
- Case studies

Learning Domains

There are generally considered to be three domains of learning:

- Cognitive: mental skills (*knowledge*)
- Psychomotor: manual or physical skills (*skills*)
- Affective: growth in feelings or emotional areas (*attitude or self*)

Bloom's Taxonomy is often used when writing learning objectives for educational or training purposes. It focuses on the cognitive, or knowledge, domain. If you need to set learning objectives, you will select a word from the taxonomy to describe what you want the learner to be able to do by the end of the training or class. Be sure to select appropriate levels of objectives for the audience, topic, and class setting (Figure 3.1).

While on the subject of learning, it is worthwhile to mention that when teaching adults, you should keep in mind the issues of physical comfort

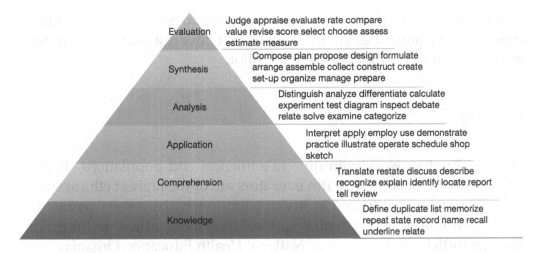

Figure 3.1 Bloom's Taxonomy

and access. Rooms should be neither too hot nor cold. There should be adequate light; the older the adults are, the more light may be needed. Consider access to accommodate a range of disabilities—how would a deaf or blind person interact with the material you were presenting? Is the building accessible to someone in a wheelchair? Will the room have what you will need to instruct your learners—whiteboards, audiovisual equipment? What will you do if a piece of the equipment fails? What is the plan if there is a medical emergency during the session? Planning for these things beforehand will pay off in the long run.

PILOT PROGRAMS

As a health educator nears the end of the planning process, there are several issues to consider. The first is integrating the heath education into other programs that may already exist in the community. In planning of health education activities, it often becomes obvious that there are clear relationships with other programs, at varying levels, to which your health education activities can be linked. Perhaps, during your planning phase, you have made some of these connections and you are going to implement your health education in connection with existing programs in communities, universities, worksites, or school systems. It is also time to think about addressing factors that will affect the implementation. **Pilot programs** are a way of testing a program or a health education material in its entirety in a limited location. This allows the health educator to discover and fix problems before a large-scale launch or decide to scrap the project altogether before investing substantial resources in a full-scale launch. If an intervention is going to be expensive, is brand new, has very limited evidence behind it, or covers a wide geographical area, it might be worth considering a pilot.

ETHICS

Health educators work with diverse audiences and populations. To help ensure that the actions of health educators are of the highest ethical standards, those who are certified as health educators by National Commission for Health Education Credentialing (NCHEC) must adhere to the guidelines set forth in the Coalition of National Health Education Organizations' (2011) *Code of Ethics for the Health Education Profession*, which can be found at www.nchec.org/code-of-ethics. It is inevitable that conflict, decisions, and even misunderstandings will arise in the course of developing, delivering, and evaluating health education across a variety of people and populations; the *Code of Ethics* provides guidance to "promote wellness and quality of living though principles of self-determination and freedom of choice."

The history of ethics in research in public health is the subject of much study. One of the most widely known, the Belmont Report, was published in 1978. The Belmont Report arose partly in response to atrocities committed during the Tuskegee Syphilis Studies and outlined procedures for the protection of human subjects during research studies. The three essential tenets are:

1. **Respect for person:** There shall be protections for the autonomy of all people and they shall be treated with courtesy, and participants shall give (and may revoke) informed consent. Researchers must be truthful and not deceive participants,with some potential exceptions under strict oversight by an institutional review board (IRB).
2. **Beneficence:** "Do no harm"—research must maximize benefits and minimize risks to participants.
3. **Justice:** Research must be fair and nonexploitative, with costs and benefits justly distributed across peoples and society.

With the publication of the Belmont Report, **IRBs** became mandated to review federally funded research protocols to ensure that research was being conducted in an appropriate manner. In practice today, many organizations and institutions have IRBs that review a range of research and intervention projects, regardless of the funding source.

CONCLUSION

The time you have spent planning, developing program goals and objectives, and piloting projects will pay off as you move to implement your program. As your program moves into the implementation phase, which we will discuss in Chapter 4, we will see how we can use tools such as logic models and timelines to make sure the program activities go as planned, adapt to new and changing information and environments, and respond to the realities of working in the real world. Chapter 4 reviews Area III: Implement Health Education/Promotion.

PRACTICE QUESTIONS

1. The level of effort of a task, who is assigned to a task, and when a task starts and stops is information that can be found in a:

   A. Logic model.
   B. Budget.
   C. Gantt chart.
   D. Strengths, weaknesses, opportunities, threats (SWOT) analysis.

2. In a community with 2,000 births in a year, five babies are born with Down syndrome. Which of the following values represent this data in a manner that allows comparison with other populations of interest?

   A. .0025
   B. 2.5%
   C. 25 per 1,000
   D. 25 per 10,000

3. A health educator at a health department wants to start a campaign to test lead levels in children in an underserved neighborhood with a high percentage of immigrants. What would be a good first step?

   A. Print brochures in English and Spanish listing testing hours and sites.
   B. Hold two community meetings.
   C. Talk with local gatekeepers to determine baseline community needs and concerns.
   D. Mandate lead testing.

4. When planning an ethnographic study and finding the most appropriate site to conduct the research, which is the least important factor for a researcher to consider?

A. Participants requesting the location
B. The researcher's ability to control the setting
C. The relevance of the site for the research interest
D. The researcher's ability to gain access to the site

5. When planning quasi-experimental designs, which is an accurate statement of their characteristics?

A. Quasi-experimental designs can control for confounding factors.
B. Quasi-experimental designs use randomization.
C. Quasi-experimental designs create the same strength of evidence as experimental designs.
D. Quasi-experimental designs do not use control groups.

6. Requiring that children younger than 2 years old ride in rear-facing car seats is an example of what kind of prevention program?

A. Health communication
B. Health marketing
C. Health policy
D. Health education

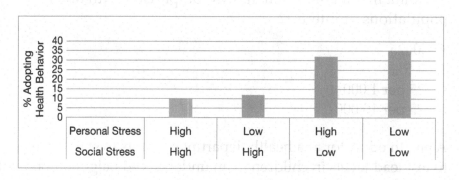

Figure 3.2 Effect of Social and Personal Stress on Adoption of Health Behavior.

7. Looking at Figure 3.2, what conclusion can you draw?

A. Personal stress is associated with an inability to adopt a health behavior.
B. Social stress is associated with an inability to adopt a health behavior.

C. Personal stress and social stress interact in the adoption of health behaviors.

D. It is impossible to draw a conclusion from the figure.

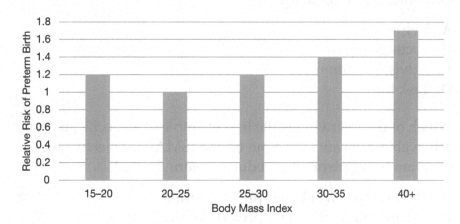

Figure 3.3 Risk of preterm birth associated with mother's body mass index risk ratio.

8. Looking at the risk of preterm birth associated with maternal body mass index (BMI) in Figure 3.3, which of the following is true?

   A. There is no association between BMI and preterm birth.
   B. Low BMI and very high BMI do not differ in risk of preterm birth.
   C. The increase in risk associated with low BMI is 40%.
   D. Both low and high BMI are associated with increased risk of preterm birth.

9. A health educator at a health department is using the data from Figure 2.2 to help plan a program to reduce preterm births. If the health educator was using the PRECEDE–PROCEED model of program planning, these data would be used during what phase of the process?

   A. Social diagnosis
   B. Epidemiological, behavioral, and environmental diagnosis
   C. Educational and ecological diagnosis
   D. Administrative and policy diagnosis

10. A health educator, in trying to reduce preterm births by helping pregnant women maintain a healthy weight, develops the Healthy Moms, Healthy Babies program. The health educator wants to gather a group of pregnant women and medical personnel to advise her on specific medical issues related to pregnancy and the

feasibility and acceptability of introducing particular activities to pregnant women as part of the program. Which type of group should the health educator convene to ensure that the best decisions are being made?

A. Delphi panel
B. Focus group
C. Advisory committee
D. Task force

11. Which of the following is the best example of a specific, measurable, achievable, relevant, and time-bound (SMART) objective for a program being planned to reduce preterm births?

A. The program will lower preterm births.
B. The program will lower preterm births by 10%.
C. By the end of year 3, Anytown, USA, will see a 10% reduction in the rate of preterm births.
D. By the end of year 3, Anytown, USA, will see a 100% reduction in the rate of preterm births.

12. "The mission of the Healthy Moms, Healthy Babies program is to ensure that all babies born in Anytown, USA, get the best start to life by helping moms have full-term pregnancies" is an example of a:

A. Goal statement
B. Specific, measurable, achievable, relevant, and time-bound (SMART) objective
C. Mission statement
D. Vision statement

13. "Healthy Moms, Healthy Babies: Ensuring that all babies are born full-term and ready to thrive" is an example of a:

A. Goal statement
B. SMART objective
C. Mission statement
D. Vision statement

14. A health educator is responsible for planning an intervention to deal with the depression and mental health issues employees face as identified by a health risk assessment in a medium-sized nonprofit

organization. Which of the following is the most appropriate program to address these problems?

A. "Lunch-and-learn" educational programs
B. Stress management programs
C. An Employee Assistance Program
D. An Alcoholics Anonymous program

15. Changing vending machines at work so that only healthier foods are offered is an example of what kind of strategy or intervention?

A. Educational
B. Environmental
C. Community mobilization
D. Health policy

16. Which one of these statements is NOT true about focus groups?

A. The results are shared with stakeholders.
B. Individual focus groups yield the richest information when participants are as diverse as possible, so that a range of opinions is represented.
C. A focus group usually lasts 1 to 2 hours.
D. Focus groups yield data that are different from data derived from individual in-depth interviews.

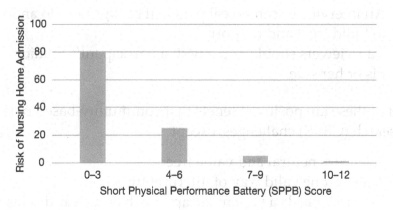

Figure 3.4 Risk of nursing home admission by SPPB.

17. The Short Physical Performance Battery (SPPB; see Figure 3.4) measures lower extremity strength. Which of the following is not true?

    A. Low scores increase nursing home admissions.

    B. The SPPB is a good tool for predicting risk of nursing home admissions over 12 months.

    C. Improving lower extremity strength might reduce nursing home admissions.

    D. The relationship between SPPB performance and nursing home admissions is linear.

18. A researcher found a statistically significant relationship between variable *X* and variable *Y* at the 0.05 alpha level. What does this mean?

    A. 95 out of 100 times, the results are true.

    B. There is a 5% chance there is a real relationship.

    C. A researcher can be 90% sure the results of the study are a reflection of the population if random sampling was used.

    D. The researcher's study is poorly designed.

19. A health educator is planning a program that would be better informed using in-depth interviews with key stakeholders of the program and gatekeepers in the community of interest. Which of the following is true about conducting in-depth interviews?

    A. Interviewers should avoid using probes or follow-up questions.

    B. Interviewers must read each question exactly as it appears on the interview questionnaire.

    C. An interviewer can reveal personal background to an interviewee to build trust and rapport.

    D. Interviewers should agree with a participant's opinion and take his or her side.

20. All of these are positivist tenets that community-based participatory research (CBPR) challenges, except:

    A. Science is neutral and value free.

    B. There is one valid way of interpreting reality.

    C. Research needs a systematic approach and clear disclosure of methods used.

    D. Because of their training, scientists are experts and their opinions carry more weight than those of community members.

ANSWERS

1. C. Gantt chart

A Gantt chart identifies who is assigned to a task, when a task begins and ends, and the intensity or level of effort a task may require in order to aid planning and monitor implementation.

2. D. 25 per 10,000

$5/2,000 = 25/10,000$. Here, 10,000 is a more standard denominator of comparison.

3. C. Talk with local gatekeepers to determine baseline community needs and concerns

Before holding community meetings, printing materials, or certainly passing rules or laws, it makes sense to speak to community gatekeepers to see where the community is on the issue.

4. B. The researcher's ability to control the setting

The relevance of the site for the research interest, the ability of the researcher to gain access, and the acceptability of the site to the population of interest are all important factors in site selection. The researcher's ability to control the dynamics setting is not only not important, but it is undesirable in qualitative research and runs counter to the ethos of conducting ethnographic research.

5. A. Quasi-experimental designs can control for confounding factors

Quasi-experimental designs can use control groups, but do not randomize participants/settings and do not generate the same strength of evidence that experimental designs do. However, they can control for confounding in the design by ensuring that the control group is as similar as possible to the treatment group in all relevant variables.

6. C. Health policy

Health policy is the field involved with laws, rules, and regulations that relate to health-promoting and disease-prevention behaviors.

7. B. Social stress is associated with an inability to adopt a health behavior

When social stress is high, the percentage of people adopting the health behavior is low, regardless of personal stress. When social stress is low, the percentage of people adopting the behavior is high, regardless of personal stress levels. Therefore, social stress, rather than personal stress, is associated with not adopting the health behavior.

8. D. Both low and high BMI are associated with increased risk of preterm birth

The data show an increased risk of preterm birth for those with low, high, and very high BMI, but the increase is only the same in the low and high categories.

9. B. Epidemiological, behavioral, and environmental diagnosis

These data fall under Phase 2 of PRECEDE–PROCEED, as they are epidemiological data.

10. C. Advisory committee

An advisory committee, or advisory board, would be the best way to get the combination of expert and lay advice that the health educator needs. A Delphi panel is used to establish consensus when there is little definitive evidence and opinion is important. Focus groups are not appropriate in this case, as you want an ongoing group to provide input. A task force is designed to work toward change, not simply to provide guidance and advice.

11. C. By the end of year 3, Anytown, USA, will see a 10% reduction in the rate of preterm births

SMART objectives need to be specific, measurable, achievable, realistic, and time bound. The difference between C and D is that a 100% reduction in the preterm birth rate, while desirable, is not achievable or realistic (unfortunately).

12. C. Mission statement

Mission statements describe the "reason for being" of the program in one sentence.

13. D. Vision statement

Vision statements describe the long-term change that the program hopes to bring about eventually. They may represent an idealized vision of the world—something to "shoot for," with the recognition that the vision is unlikely to ever be fully realized.

14. C. An Employee Assistance Program

An Employee Assistance Program (EAP) is a voluntary, work-based program, paid for by the employer, that offers free (to the employee), confidential assessments, short-term counseling, referrals, and follow-up services to employees who have personal and/or work-related problems. EAPs address issues such as alcohol and substance abuse, stress, grief, family problems, and psychological disorders.

15. B. Environmental

By changing the food that is available to people, you have changed the environment in which they work.

16. B. Individual focus groups yield the richest information when participants are as diverse as possible, so that a range of opinions is represented

When conducting focus groups, it is best for them to be as homogeneous as possible, especially around variables of interest or if a topic is particularly sensitive, to encourage discussion. For instance, you would probably want to segregate focus groups by gender to discuss areas around sexual health, or by race to discuss issues that affect races differently. This can allow people to express opinions more honestly and without fear of giving offense, and allow the respondents to "warm up" in a room full of strangers more quickly—which is always important when time to collect data is limited.

17. D. The relationship between SPPB performance and nursing home admissions is linear

The relationship between SPPB performance and nursing home admission is closer to exponential than linear.

18. A. 95 out of 100 times, the results are true

A 0.05 alpha level means that five out of 100 times, the results would not occur naturally.

19. C. Interviewers can reveal their personal background to the interviewee to build trust and rapport

It is not unusual for interviewees to ask questions of the interviewer. Disclosing personal information (appropriately) "levels the field" and often helps generate trust. Also, refusing to answer participant's questions may generate suspicion.

20. C. Research needs a systematic approach and clear disclosure of methods used

All research, regardless of paradigm, must follow systematic procedures, and the methods should be disclosed so the research can be understood and critiqued.

REFERENCES

Centers for Disease Control and Prevention. (2016a). A framework for program evaluation. Retrieved from http://www.cdc.gov/eval/framework/index.htm

Centers for Disease Control and Prevention. (2016b). Developing program goals and measurable objectives. Retrieved from https://www.cdc.gov/std/program/pupestd/developing%20program%20goals%20and%20objectives.pdf

Centers for Disease Control and Prevention. (2016c). Planning, implementing, and evaluating an intervention—An overview. Retrieved from www.cdc.gov/violenceprevention/pdf/chapter1-a.pdf

Coalition of National Health Education Organizations. (2011). Code of Ethics For the Health Education Profession. Available at: http://www.cnheo.org/files/coe_full_2011.pdf

Community Tool Box. (2016). Proclaiming your dream: Developing vision and mission statements (Chapter 8, Section 2). Retrieved from http://www.ctb.ku.edu/en/table-of-contents/overview/models-for-community-health-and-development/healthy-cities-healthy-communities/main

Glanz, K., Rimer, B. K., & Viswanath, K. (Eds.). (2008). *Health behavior and health education: Theory, research, and practice* (4th ed.). San Francisco, CA: Jossey-Bass.

Glanz, K., & Rimer, B. K. (2005). *Theory at a glance: A guide to health promotion practice* (2nd ed.). (NIH Publ. 05-3896). Bethesda, MD: National Cancer Institute.

National Commission for the Protection of Human Subjects of Biomedical and Behavioral Research, Department of Health, Education and Welfare (1978, April 18). *The Belmont report*. Retrieved from -->https://www.hhs.gov/ohrp/sites/default/files/the-belmont-report-508c_FINAL.pdf

National Network of Libraries of Medicine. (2016). *Community-based organization defined*. Retrieved from https://nnlm.gov/sea/funding/cbodef.html

Rossi, P. H., Lipsey, M. W., & Freeman, H. E. (2004). Expressing and assessing program theory. In *Evaluation: A systematic approach* (7th ed., pp. 133–168). Thousand Oaks, CA: Sage.

Rowel, R., Moore, N. D., Nowrojee, S., Memiah, P., & Bronner, Y. (2005). The utility of the environmental scan for public health practice: Lessons from an urban program to increase cancer screening. *Journal of the National Medical Association, 97*(4), 527–534. Retrieved from https://www.ncbi.nlm.nih.gov/pmc/articles/PMC2568702

Warrick, C., Culica, D., Quill, B. E., Spears, W., & Vojvodic, R. W. (2005). Community development and public health. In L. A. Aday (Ed.), *Reinventing public health: Policies and practices for a healthy nation* (pp. 237–284). San Francisco, CA: Jossey-Bass.

Wholey, J. S., Hatry, H. P., & Newcomer, K. E. (2010). *Handbook of practical program evaluation*. Hoboken, NJ: John Wiley & Sons.

Chapter 4

Area III: Implement Health Education/ Promotion

INTRODUCTION

Once needs have been assessed and programs have been planned, it is time for them to be implemented. Implementation is the time when "the rubber hits the road," and as a health educator you get to see how all that needs assessment, audience research, goal setting, theory selection, message development, and program planning is going to work in the real world. In a classroom setting is where the actual teaching occurs, tests are given, and teaching assistants are trained. In a community or worksite setting, you may be providing cooking demonstrations, walking groups, or swapping out junk food for fruit in vending machines, while making sure that the program is going according to plan and everyone involved knows what they are supposed to do and when. While a thorough job in the assessment and planning stages will serve you well, there is still a lot to learn and do in this phase.

IMPLEMENT A PLAN OF ACTION

According to McKenzie, Neigher, and Thackery (2016), there are five phases of implementation:

1. Adopting the program
2. Identifying and prioritizing tasks
3. Establishing a management system

4. Enacting the plan

5. Ending or sustaining the program

In the following section, we discuss what is needed to optimize program implementation.

The first step in the area of implementation is actually more planning. As you have probably noticed by now, health educators spend a lot of their time planning! First, let us define what we mean by "implementation." Implementation is when we put our plans into action—when we launch and run the program. In a training program, that could be recruiting for and holding the trainings. At a hospital, we might launch a flu shot campaign and spend 6 weeks promoting the availability of flu shots through posters, emails, lunch and learns, and incentive programs. In a community setting, we might improve physical activity rates by improving awareness through local media, partnering with parks to provide daily walking tours, promoting low-cost classes held at community centers, or working with schools to increase the time students spend at recess. All of those are examples of program implementation. Developing and following a plan for implementation– an action plan—will help keep things running smoothly. The action plan should include a step-by-step accounting of everything that needs to happen, who is responsible for it, any materials or items necessary, and what to do if something goes wrong.

Assess Readiness for Implementation[1]

While considerable effort may have already gone into the development of a program, now is the time to assess how ready your program is for implementation. Look at the plan you created. What needs does it have in terms of resources—staffing, funding, partners, equipment, and so on? This is the time to make sure that the goals and objectives you set are achievable with the resources you have. For instance, if you planned on holding educational sessions at a local library and you discover now that the conference room is being renovated, you need to rethink your plans before you go any further. Likewise, if in the planning process you have now added additional parts of the intervention, such as increasing access to screenings by keeping the clinic open 2 additional hours 3 days a week, you need to make sure that you have the funding and the staff to make that actually happen.

---

[1] NCHEC Competency 3.1. Coordinate logistics necessary to implement plan.

Collect Baseline Data

As you can likely anticipate, evaluation is critical to a comprehensive health education program. If the purpose of evaluation is to find out what changes a program made, then we have to know what the situation was BEFORE the program was launched. This is the time to collect baseline data—both qualitative and quantitative—so we have an accurate BEFORE picture. Quantitative and qualitative data are reviewed in Chapter 2, so please refer to them for a more in-depth discussion of the methods available to you as a health educator.

As a health educator, you will have to decide whether you need to collect **primary** or **secondary** data at this stage. **Primary data** are those data you collect yourself. These could come from surveys, focus groups, in-depth interviews, observations of current behavior, sales receipts, and so on. The key is that this is the data your program has specifically collected to serve in understanding what is going on in the primary, secondary, or tertiary audience or the setting in which an intervention is to take place. Primary data collection has the advantage of being customizable to answer the specific needs of your program, but it can be costly and time consuming to collect, analyze, and interpret these data. **Secondary data**, on the other hand, are the data collected for another purpose that might be useful or applicable for your intervention. Examples of secondary data sources are the Behavioral Risk Factor Surveillance System (www.cdc.gov/brfss), U.S. Census Bureau's American Fact Finder (factfinder.census.gov/faces/nav/jsf/pages/index.xhtml), and the National Center for Health Statistics (www.cdc.gov/nchs) A listing of many publicly available secondary data sets is available at www.cdc.gov/stltpublichealth/cha/data.html. **Indicators** are a kind of secondary data that can be used to compare rates of or trends in health outcomes or determinants. The advantage of using secondary data is that it has been collected and often analyzed for you, dramatically reducing your cost and time investment. The challenge, of course, is that it was collected to meet somebody else's needs and may not fully answer all the questions for your program. As a health educator, it is part of your job to balance the desire for program-specific information with the budgetary and time constraints of your project to come up with baseline data that tell you what you need to know to implement your program well.

Collecting your baseline data, be it primary, secondary, or a combination, means having thought through your evaluation plan. We will talk about evaluation in Chapter 5, but once you have made your evaluation plan, you will have to implement the baseline data collection before you launch your program.

Cultural Competence

Cultural competence—what does that even mean? Scholars and experts do not agree how to create culturally competent programs, and, really, even a definition is hard to come by. We all exist within many cultures—our racial or ethnic culture, the culture of our region or state or hometown, the culture of work, our school, our neighborhood, our friends, our religion, our place of worship. Whole books have been written on cultural competency relevant to health education. One of the most commonly used definitions identifies cultural and linguistic competencies as a set of congruent behaviors, knowledge, attitudes, and policies that come together in a system, organization, or among professionals that enables effective work in cross-cultural situations. "Culture" refers to integrated patterns of human behavior that include the language, thoughts, actions, customs, beliefs, and institutions of racial, ethnic, social, or religious groups. "Competence" implies having the capacity to function effectively as an individual or an organization within the context of the cultural beliefs, practices, and needs presented by patients and their communities.

Principles of cultural competence include:

1. Define culture broadly.
2. Value clients' cultural beliefs.
3. Recognize complexity in language interpretation.
4. Facilitate learning between providers and communities.
5. Involve the community in defining and addressing service needs.
6. Collaborate with other agencies.
7. Professionalize staff hiring and training.
8. Institutionalize cultural competence.

(Centers for Disease Control and Prevention, National Prevention Information Network, 2015)

While navigating the waters of cultural competency can be tricky, let us remember why it is important to keep culture in mind. Race, gender, ethnicity, country/region of origin, religious affiliation, and education level all contribute to health disparities. Providing care, including health education, to people with diverse values, beliefs, and behaviors is critical to narrowing the gaps in health status. According to the Health Research and Educational Trust (2013), the benefits of cultural competency include social benefits such as increased mutual respect between patient and organization, increased community participation in health issues, health benefits such as increased preventative care and cost savings, and business benefits such as compliance with legal and regulatory guidelines and improvements in efficiency.

Further Reading

Center for the Application of Prevention Technologies, Substance Abuse and Mental Health Services Administration. (2016). Cultural Competence. Retrieved from www.samhsa.gov/capt/applying-strategic-prevention/cultural-competence

Office of Communication and Public Liaison, National Institutes of Health. (2017). Cultural Respect. Retrieved from www.nih.gov/institutes-nih/nih-office-director/office-communications-public-liaison/clear-communication/cultural-respect

Culture affects nearly everything people encounter in their daily lives—including how people communicate, comprehend, and respond to health information. Having culturally and linguistically competent health professionals can contribute to health literacy. Part of cultural competence is the ability of health organizations and practitioners to recognize the cultural beliefs, values, attitudes, traditions, language preferences, and health practices of diverse populations, and to apply that knowledge to help produce positive health outcomes.

It is crucial to recognize that health education professionals have our own culture and language, and those affect how we communicate with the public. Words like "incidence" and "prevalence" seem normal to us, as do the reasons we use them. Recognize that this information, and much more, may not be accessible—or accepted—by everyone.

For many individuals with limited English proficiency (LEP), the inability to communicate in English is a crucial barrier to accessing health information and services. Health information for people with LEP needs to be communicated plainly in their primary language, using words and examples that make the information understandable. Finding and employing interpreters who can communicate in culturally competent ways with people with LEP is a sensitive and important task, as is producing materials for people with LEP in their language of choice. Not only do the same "plain language" rules apply, but we must remember that people may or may not be literate in their preferred language. The way we think about health, illness, mental illness, nutrition, and so on may not be the way other cultures approach the same issues. To be truly culturally competent (if such a thing is even possible) requires a thorough understanding of not only the audience, but also of our own cultural perspectives and assumptions. It is a task of a lifetime—one that a health educator must understand can never be fully achieved.

Select From Appropriate Intervention Strategies to Achieve Goals

One of the mistakes health educators can make is to narrowly limit the strategies they use when implementing programs. As we have seen in Chapters 2 and 3, audiences can vary widely in their knowledge, locations, preferences, learning styles, and so on. Therefore, it is important to employ a variety of intervention strategies to ensure that we reach as many people in as many ways as feasible for a particular project.

Potential intervention strategies include:

Individual level

- Trainings
- Coaching sessions
- Counseling sessions
- Personalized communications
- Interpersonal communication
- Medical interventions

Group level

- Classes
- Neighborhood environmental interventions (playgrounds, parks)
- Church/school/civic organization trainings/distributions, and so on

Mass level

- Mass communications
  - TV
  - Radio
  - Websites
  - Podcasts

- Facebook/Twitter/Instagram
- Brochures
- Posters
- Leaflets
- Policy interventions
- Announcements and public events

How to select appropriate intervention strategies? Insights from formative research, published literature, and expert advice from consultants will all help guide you, but your budgetary and time constraints likely will be your biggest factors. Just remember to think creatively and consider what is needed to achieve your program's objectives.

Tailor Messages to Distinct Subgroups

Audience segmentation is an important technique for making sure that messages and interventions meet the unique and possibly contradictory needs of different audiences. By segmenting, or tailoring, messages to distinct subgroups, health educators can address the specific needs, beliefs, and behaviors of each group. At first blush, many health educators consider demographics such as age, race, or sex as characteristics on which to tailor materials. However, there are often considerably more effective characteristics to consider. Consider the stage of change (see the following section and Chapter 8) your participants are in—those in precontemplation (those not considering change) may need awareness-raising messages to get them thinking about why a change might be necessary, while those already in action may need supportive or reinforcement messages. Knowing what your population has reached is critical for ensuring the right messages get to the right people.

Similarly, sometimes messages are segmented in a doer/nondoer dichotomy. People eating five servings a day of fruits and vegetables may need reinforcement for doing so in order to stave off boredom, or they might be willing to spread the message to their friends and family. Those who are not eating much in the way of fruits and vegetables may need encouragement to add, say, one serving a day. Both groups might be interested in recipes, coupons, or tips, but how those tools are presented may need to be different. Similarly, messages on sex, pregnancy, and child care are more likely to be effective if they are tailored to novices or to those with considerable experience. A third-time mother likely is looking for very different information (reminders or recommendations that have changed since her last pregnancy) in very different formats (quick and easy) than a first-time mother, to whom everything is new.

There are as many segmentation strategies as there are audiences. Knowing to whom you are speaking and what their needs/concerns are will help you identify the correct behavior-change strategy.

APPLY RELEVANT THEORIES OF BEHAVIOR CHANGE AND MODELS OF IMPLEMENTATION

There is nothing so practical as good theory.

—Kurt Lewin

Dr. Lewin's famous words are as relevant today as they were when he uttered them in the 1940s. Without a firm understanding of their audience and how human behavior changes, health educators are doomed to randomly try different interventions with no specific insight into how they might be successful. This section reviews several relevant behavioral and organizational change theories. A fuller review of such theories can be found in Appendix B of the National Cancer Institute's (2002) *Making Health Communication Programs Work: A Planner's Guide* ("The Pink Book") and Chapter 2 of the National Institute of Medicine's *Speaking of Health: Assessing Communication Strategies for Diverse Populations* (2002).

Individual-Level Theories

Health Belief Model

The Health Belief Model (HBM) was developed to help understand why people choose not to participate in programs to prevent or detect disease. The core constructs of the HBM are:

- **Perceived susceptibility**—The perception of the individual of how at risk they are of developing a particular condition.
- **Perceived severity**—The perception of the individual of how severe or serious the consequences would be of developing a particular condition.
- **Perceived benefits**—The individual's beliefs of how effective or beneficial certain actions (e.g., screenings, preventative behavior) would be at reducing a particular health threat.

- **Perceived barriers**—The individual's perception of conditions, actions, or consequences that might prevent them from taking the proposed preventive action (e.g., cost, pain, fear, time).

- **Cues to action**—Environmental or individual factors that encourage the preventive behavior.

- **Self-efficacy**—The individual's perceived ability to perform the behavior. This a more recent addition to HBM that was included to expand the applicability of HBM into more long-term, complex behaviors, such as chronic-disease prevention and lifestyle-change programs.

FURTHER READING

Champion, V. L., & Skinner, C. S. (2006). The health belief model. In K. Glanz, F. M. Lewis, & B. K Rimer (Eds.), *Health behavior and health education: Theory, research, and practice* (4th ed.). San Francisco, CA: Jossey-Bass.

Theory of Reasoned Action/Theory of Planned Behavior

The Integrated Behavioral Model comes out of the long history of the Theory of Reasoned Action/Theory of Planned Behavior (TRA/TPB). (Fishbein & Ajzen, 1975). The TRA/TPB posited that behavioral intention, that is, a person's intention to perform a particular behavior and their perceived control over that behavior, were the most important predictors of whether an individual would actually perform a behavior. The TRA contained four basic constructs:

- *Behavioral Beliefs*—The beliefs a person has toward the outcome of performing a particular behavior.

- *Evaluations of Behavioral Outcomes*—The weight a person gives to what the likely outcome a behavior will have.

These first two constructs combine to create an individual's attitude toward a behavior. People with strong beliefs that a behavior will benefit them will have a positive attitude toward the behavior.

- *Normative beliefs*—How an individual perceives that people he or she cares about perceive the behavior.

- *Motivation to comply*—How motivated a person is by his or her normative beliefs.

These last two constructs combine to form one's Subjective Norms.
The TPB, updated in the 1980s and 1990s (Ajzen & Madden, 1986; Azjen, 1991) added two additional constructs:

- *Control beliefs*—Positive and negative factors to allow the behavior to be performed.
- *Percieved power*—How important those facilitators or barriers are to the behavior.

FURTHER READING

Montaño, D. E., & Kasprzyk, D. (2006). Theory of reasoned action, theory of planned behavior, and the integrated behavioral model. In K. Glanz, F. M. Lewis, & B. K. Rimer (Eds.), *Health behavior and health education: Theory, research, and practice* (4th ed.). San Francisco, CA: Jossey-Bass.

Transtheoretical Model

The Transtheoretical Model (TTM) posits that behavior change is a continually evolving process rather than a one-time event. An underlying assumption of the model is that individuals are at varying levels of motivation, or readiness to change, for each behavior at any particular time. People at different stages of change need different interventions matched to where they are at a particular time. By knowing where an individual is, you can design appropriate and realistic interventions to move the individual farther along the continuum of behavior change.

There are five stages of behavior change in the model:

1. *Precontemplation*—The person is not thinking about changing the behavior.
2. *Contemplation*—The person is aware of the need for behavior change and is considering changing the behavior.
3. *Preparation*—The person has decided to change the behavior and is preparing to do so.
4. *Action*—The person is actively changing the behavior.
5. *Maintenance*—The person has changed the behavior and is adopting it as the new normal.

While it is tempting to think of this process as linear and progressive, it is not. People enter and exit the model at different stages and often revert to an earlier stage, or "fail" at behavior change/maintenance, and start over again somewhere on the continuum.

FURTHER READING

Prochaska, J. O., Redding, C. A., & Evers, K. E. (2008). The transtheoretical model and stages of change. In K. Glanz, F. M. Lewis, & B. K. Rimer (Eds.), *Health behavior and health education: Theory, research, and practice* (4th ed.). San Francisco, CA: Jossey-Bass.

Prochaska, J. O., & Velicer, W. F. (1997). The transtheoretical model of health behavior change. *American Journal of Health Promotion, 12*(1), 38–48. doi:10.4278/0890-1171-12.1.38

Communication for Persuasion

McGuire's Persuasive Communication strategy describes the components of successful communication:

1. Credible message source ("*sender*")
2. Intended audience ("*receiver*")
3. Delivery *channel*
4. *Message* design
5. Intended behavioral *response*

McGuire also described 12 steps through which a message must go to create behavior change. These steps also give evaluators an opportunity to see where a message may have failed, for each step is linear and progressive. The 12 steps are:

1. Exposure to the message
2. Attention to the message
3. Interest in/personal relevance seen in the message
4. Understanding the message
5. Ability to adapt the message to one's own situation
6. Believing the message
7. Remembering the message in the appropriate context
8. Being able to do the behavior in the message
9. Making the decision to actually do the behavior when one thinks of it
10. Making the behavior change

11. Being reinforced for the behavior

12. Maintaining the behavior

FURTHER READING

McGuire, W. J. (1984). Public communication as a strategy for inducing health-promoting behavioral change. *Preventive Medicine, 13*(3), 299–313. doi:10.1016/0091-7435(84)90086-0

Elaboration Likelihood Model

The Elaboration Likelihood Model (ELM) posits that if people are engaged or interested in a particular behavior, then they will pay more attention to (elaborate on) new information presented to them about the behavior. If people are not already engaged on an issue, they will require additional stimuli (e.g., peripheral cues such as a spokesperson, models, colors, or music) to be persuaded. Beliefs and behaviors developed under the peripheral processing route are less durable than those developed under the central processing route, and therefore require frequent reinforcement.

Advertisers often use this model to design messages. An advertisement for a product that people care less about—say, toothpaste—will likely use lots of peripheral cues—an attractive model, cute slogans, catchy jingles—to help persuade the viewer that Brand A of toothpaste is the one to buy. Something in which the viewer is more interested, however—like information on a disease that the person has recently been diagnosed with—will be more centrally processed and judged on the merits of the message, not on the message heuristics.

FURTHER READING

Petty, R., & Cacioppo, J. (1986). *Communication and persuasion: Central and peripheral routes to attitude change.* New York, NY: Springer-Verlag.

Extended Parallel Processing Model

The Extended Parallel Processing Model (EPPM) helps understand how fear of a particular outcome may influence a person's decision-making process. The EPPM has four constructs to predict the likely outcome of communications that use a fear appeal:

- **Self-efficacy**—The extent to which a person believes that he or she is able to control the risk.
- **Response efficacy**—The extent to which a person believes that the suggested action, if carried out, will successfully control the risk.
- **Susceptibility**—The perception the person has of how likely the threat will affect him or her.
- **Severity**—The perception the person has of how serious the threat is.

Based on these four constructs, the theory predicts one of three possible outcomes to communication materials:

1. **Danger control**—When a person perceives that the severity and susceptibility are high and also perceives that he or she is competent to make changes, then he or she is likely to act to control the danger.
2. **Fear control**—The model predicts that if a person perceives their ability to control a risk as low, even if the severity and susceptibility is perceived as high, then they are likely to take steps to control their fear instead. This is undesirable because it does not lead to the desired behavior change; rather, it may lead to denial or fatalism. Many people consider it unethical to use fear-based messages in this situation because they may cause more harm than good. Steps must first be taken to raise an individual's self-efficacy before fear messages may safely and effectively be used.
3. **No response**—The severity or susceptibility of the danger was perceived as low; therefore, the person made no changes.

FURTHER READING

Witte, K. (1994). Fear control and danger control: A test of the extended parallel process model. *Communication Monographs, 61*(2), 113–134. doi:10.1080/03637759409376328

Interpersonal Level Theories

Social Cognitive Theory

Social Cognitive Theory (SCT) is the most commonly cited interpersonal-level theory a health educator is likely to use. SCT operates on the idea that an individual's behavior is the result of ongoing interactions between his or her internal psychosocial traits and the external environment in which he or she operates—called reciprocal determinism. Perhaps the most widely used construct from SCT is self-efficacy—an individual's belief that he or she can carry out a particular behavior and overcome any barriers to performing the behavior. There are several additional constructs in the theory:

- Behavioral capability
- Expectations
- Expectancies
- Self-control
- Emotional coping responses

FURTHER READING

Bandura, A. (2002). Social cognitive theory of mass communication. In J. Bryant & M. B. Oliver (Eds.), *Media effects: Advances in theory and research* (pp. 94–124). New York, NY: Routledge.

Organizational/Community Level Theories

Diffusion of Innovation Theory

Diffusion of Innovation Theory describes how products, ideas, and/or social practices or norms that are perceived as "new" spread throughout a population. Diffusion theory has been used to study the adoption of a wide range of technologies and behaviors, including health behaviors and programs.

According to the theory, for any given innovation, people's adoption of the behavior or technology can be categorized as one of the following:

1. Innovators (2.5%)
2. Early adaptors (13.5%)
3. Early majority (34%)
4. Late majority (34%)
5. Laggards (16%)

According to Diffusion of Innovation Theory, diffusion occurs through a five-step process through which people make decisions. The five stages are the following:

1. Knowledge—person becomes aware of innovation.
2. Persuasion—person becomes interested in learning more about the innovation.
3. Decision—person decides to adopt or reject the innovation.
4. Implementation—if the decision is made to adopt, implementation (of varying degrees) occurs. Further information gathering may occur.
5. Confirmation—The person finalizes the decision to adopt, working through internal issues (cognitive dissonance) or social interactions to confirm the adoption was desirable.

FURTHER READING

Rogers, E. M. (1962). *Diffusion of innovations*. New York, NY: Free Press of Glencoe.

Stage Theory

Stage Theory is based on the idea that organizations move through a series of predictable stages as they change. This is helpful for understanding where organizations are in the change process, so as to be able to match activities to the organization's stage of change. In the 1940s, Lewin proposed three stages: Unfreeze, Change, and Refreeze.

Modern Stage Theory takes Lewin's work and combines it with Rogers' Diffusion of Innovations Theory to create four stages of organizational change:

1. Developing the awareness of a problem and possible solutions.
2. Deciding to adopt a change or innovation.
3. Implementing the change (including changing organizational structures/supports).
4. Institutionalizing the change and making it part of the organization's structure/activities.

FURTHER READING

Butterfoss, F. D., Kegler, M. C., & Francisco, V. T. (2008). Mobilizing organizations for health promotion: Theories of organizational change. In K. Glanz, F. M. Lewis, & B.

K. Rimer (Eds.), *Health behavior and health education: Theory, research, and practice* (4th ed.). San Francisco, CA: Jossey-Bass.

IMPLEMENT PROGRAM[2]

Before implementing your program, use this checklist to ensure you are ready for a successful launch:

☑ Are all partners prepared for the launch?
☑ Have we invited reviewers, gatekeepers, and other stakeholders who have been involved in the program development?
☑ Have we trained project staff and spokespeople?
☑ Are program-related services (such as hotlines, screening tests, materials) in place?
☑ Is there a media plan in place?
☑ Are all program-related materials ready?
☑ Do we have enough program-related materials to begin the program and respond to media/public inquiries?
☑ Do we have a way to get more materials if they are necessary?
☑ Is there a monitoring plan in place?
☑ Are other health-related professionals in the community aware of the program and ready to respond to their clients if they are asked about it?

(*Source*: Adapted from National Cancer Institute, 2002)

Once your audiences have been identified and segmented; your messages, trainings, and interventions crafted and reviewed for cultural competence; and your channels selected, it is time to launch your program! There are several possibilities for how to do this, each with their own plusses and minuses. Many times, a health educator starts by launching a pilot program. Pilot programs are, by design, small, and may address onlyone audience or location. The goal of a pilot program is to work out the "kinks" and see what works or what does not work in the implementation. Positive aspects of a pilot program are that they give you a real-world yet manageable idea of how the audience thinks and feels, and what it will do with your program. If mistakes are made or pieces of the intervention are inadequate or redundant, you can find this out while there is time and money to correct problems. You will likely to learn a lot about the differences between a program on paper and conducting one in a real setting—information that can help you revise and improve your program. Are people receptive to what you are trying to do? Do they understand your materials? Do they feel safe working with the program? Do they believe what you are telling them? Does the intervention

---

[2] NCHEC Competency 3.3. Implement health education/promotion plan.

take longer than you predicted to have a desired result? The downside of a pilot program is that it costs money, takes time, and the things you learn in your pilot may not be generalizable to your full implementation. Still, a pilot can be a very valuable tool and should be employed if at all feasible.

If you have piloted your program and made revisions, you may move to a phase-in approach to implementation. A phase-in approach is the middle ground between your pilot and full implementation. Perhaps you offer it to all audiences in one geographic area, or one type of audience across your geographic areas. Or you start with one part of the implementation and save other parts for later. A phase-in approach also has the benefit of simplifying what you are doing so it is easier to spot problems and correct them. But the case where something is urgently needed, such as information on an emerging infectious disease, it is unlikely that you will be able to take the time.

The full implementation, whether it happens after a pilot or phase-in implementation, is your final stage of implementation. Next, you will begin monitoring your implementation to ensure that it is going according to plan.

Training for Implementation[3]

Many implementation errors and challenges can be prevented by proper training. While we often think of training our populations of interest (such as providing cooking classes or car-seat installation sessions), program staff should be trained on program implementation as well. The more complex the implementation, the more important training becomes. One document that will need to be developed for training is a **Manual of Procedures (MOP)**. A MOP is a document, often in the form of a handbook or binder, that details a project's or study's operations and procedures and facilitates consistency in implementation and data collection across project participants and sites.

For example, say you are implementing an evidence-based teen pregnancy prevention program in a school system. The program has been previously demonstrated to be effective as written, which means it needs to be delivered as written to have the greatest chance of success. Teachers need to be trained, therefore, on all the components of the program, with an emphasis on delivering the training as it is written. Too often in such

---

[3] NCHEC Competency 3.2. Train staff members and volunteers involved in implementation of education/promotion.

implementations, program drift occurs—the delivered materials move away from the intervention as planned, either deliberately or due to carelessness. Those delivering the intervention need to be trained on the importance of delivering the intervention as intended. During the training is a good time to ask for feedback on challenges or concerns that those delivering the intervention might have. In this example, teachers may note that in their school system, classes are 50 minutes long, rather than the 55 minutes the curriculum allows. Training can be a time to make minor adjustments to the implementation to suit local needs. Likewise, if those implementing the program are uncomfortable with certain topics, training can help them overcome their anxieties and convince them of the need to deliver the program as intended.

Another important part is training project implementers on how and when to report changes, deviations, or problems that occur during implementation. Developing a structure for reporting these issues will allow project managers to respond quickly to any problems. Using our previous example of the teen pregnancy prevention program, say it was scheduled after school on Wednesdays for 8 consecutive weeks. If students miss weeks four and five due to snow days and attendance was very low on week seven due to illness, program managers need to be alerted in real time so they can make adjustments. Otherwise, 3 of the 8 weeks of curriculum will have been missed and the project will be unlikely to meet its objectives.

MONITORING IMPLEMENTATION[4]

Often overlooked in favor of evaluation, monitoring is a critical piece of the implementation process and should be planned with the implementation from the beginning. Monitoring has two specific purposes: to make sure that the implementation happens as it was planned and to identify any unforeseen or unexpected issues or events that may affect the project's implementation or outcomes. Monitoring is "keeping your fingers on the pulse" of the implementation so you can quickly respond with corrections to your implementation as needed.

Issues you need to periodically assess include:

- Are activities being completed at scheduled times?
- Are your intended audiences being reached?
- Which materials are being used more successfully? Less successfully?

---

[4]   NCHEC Competency 3.4. Monitor implementation of health education/promotion.

- Are there activities that need to be expanded or eliminated?
- Are you within budget?

Program management should maintain an open-door policy and attitude around program implementation and monitoring, and MOPs should be updated regularly to reflect lessons learned in the implementation. All program staff, participants, and stakeholders should be encouraged to bring concerns to the attention of the program management team as soon as possible, so that concerns can be addressed before they reduce the likelihood of the program being effective. Likewise, things that are going well in implementation should also be noted so they can be scaled in more effective ways.

Project Timelines

Project timelines, often known as Gantt charts, are a way of helping to plan and monitor how a project is implemented. They help visualize what tasks must be done before another task can be completed, and what steps are necessary to bring a project to fruition. They are an excellent monitoring tool to provide the user the ability to look at the chart on any given day and see if the project is running on time, what has been completed, and what lies ahead. There are a number of project management software solutions for creating project timelines, or they may be created in a spreadsheet program like Excel. Figure 4.1 shows a template created in Excel for a 10-week, simple program that requires

Task	Who is responsible?	Week 1	Week 2	Week 3	Week 4	Week 5	Week 6	Week 7	Week 8	Week 9	Week 10
Administration											
Task 1											
Task 2											
Task 3											
Task 4											
Task 5											
Material Development											
Task 1											
Task 2											
Task 3											
Task 4											
Task 5											
Task 6											
Task 7											
Evaluation											
Task 1											
Task 2											
Task 3											

Figure 4.1 Example of a project management spreadsheet.

material development and evaluation. The more complex an intervention, the more complex the project timeline is likely to be. Using color and subheadings to distinguish among different phases or areas of responsibility can help keep complex timelines more manageable.

CONCLUSION

This chapter provided an overview of strategies and competencies needed to successfully implement health education programs and interventions. It is important to consider the process of implementation, the application theories of behavior change, cultural competence, training, and monitoring of implementation. In Chapter 5, you will review Area IV: Conduct Evaluation and Research Related to Health Education/ Promotion.

REVIEW QUESTIONS

1. Which is NOT a part of a theory?

    A. Concepts
    B. Definitions
    C. Propositions
    D. Conclusions

2. In a research study, the requirement of "informed consent" has to do with which ethical principle?

    A. Universalism
    B. Beneficence
    C. Respect for individuals
    D. Do no harm

3. Which action do you NOT take in the literature review of a proposal?

    A. Build an argument for the study.
    B. Demonstrate the relevance of the study.
    C. Describe how you will measure variables in your study.
    D. Present epidemiologic data related to the issue under study.

4. For which of these tasks is a reference manager such as EndNote NOT helpful?

   A. Permit you to cite what you write easily.
   B. Change your references from APA style to AMA format quickly.
   C. Decide which citations should be used for justifying your study.
   D. Store all your references in one place.

5. According to the transtheoretical model, as an individual moved from precontemplation into maintenance, the lessening of negative beliefs and increasing of positive beliefs about a behavior is best described as:

   A. Self-actualization
   B. Self-efficacy
   C. Decisional balance
   D. Perception of benefits

6. For employees who quit smoking last week, what would be the most effective strategy for supporting them in their cessation attempt?

   A. Sending them information on the harms done by tobacco to the body
   B. Sending them graphic videos of the harms that tobacco does to the body
   C. Sending them messages about how most of their fellow employees do not use tobacco
   D. Sending a congratulatory note for having made it through the first week

7. A participant in a program states, "As a woman who did not ever breastfeed, I am at higher risk for breast cancer." Which of the following constructs of the Health Belief Model does this statement best demonstrate?

   A. Perceived barrier
   B. Perceived susceptibility
   C. Self-efficacy
   D. Cue to action

8. A health educator is implementing a pilot project where rapid response teams are available to go into communities that have been affected by gun violence and provide grief counseling and support. If the program shows positive outcomes, it will be expanded. To ensure fidelity to intervention and track lessons learned during the implementation, the health educator should develop an MOP, which stands for:

   A. Manual on Places
   B. Manual of Plans
   C. Manual of Procedures
   D. Manual of Priorities

9. The Theory of Planned Behavior is a theory of health behavior aimed at which of the following levels?

   A. Individual
   B. Community
   C. Organizational
   D. Population

10. Identifying theories of behavior change and best practice models allows you to:

    A. Eliminate the need to do research on the audience.
    B. Predict the success of an intervention strategy with precision.
    C. Narrow the cause of a health problem to a single theory or model to make it easier to conceptualize and plan an intervention.
    D. Identify determinants that lead people to problem behaviors and develop programs that are more likely to be successful in influencing the behavior.

11. All of the following types of interventions may pose barriers to the dissemination of evidence-based programs, except:

    A. Interventions that lack flexibility
    B. Interventions that account for user's needs and preferences
    C. Interventions that have a high degree of technical sophistication
    D. Interventions that have garnered limited organizational support

12. The time to consider the sustainability of an implementation of a program or study is:

    A. In the planning stages
    B. At the beginning of implementation
    C. At the halfway mark
    D. At the end of the first round of funding

13. All of the following can be used to monitor implementation and progress toward goals and objectives, except:

    A. Gantt chart
    B. PERT
    C. CPM
    D. EBMR

14. Which of the following would be the correct order of steps when implementing a worksite health promotion program to reduce back injuries?

    A. Introduce the program to management, do a health risk assessment, introduce the program to employees, and schedule trainings
    B. Introduce the program to management, introduce the program to employees, do a health risk assessment, and schedule trainings
    C. Introduce the program to employees, introduce the program to management, do a health risk assessment, and schedule trainings
    D. Do a health risk assessment, introduce the program to management, introduce the program to employees, and schedule trainings

15. All of the following are reasonable approaches to take when the demand for a project exceeds project resources, except:

    A. Screening or wait-listing participants on a preset criteria
    B. Referring those not selected for an intervention to community resources
    C. Selecting those most at need for the intervention
    D. Selecting only one demographic group to serve for convenience of data collection

16. A health educator at a worksite is developing a health risk assessment. He writes, "Are you planning on quitting smoking in the next 30 days?" Which theory of change is the health educator using?

    A. Theory of Planned Behavior
    B. Theory of Reasoned Action
    C. Transtheoretical Model
    D. Social Cognitive Theory

17. In what stage of change would a smoker be who was planning on quitting in the next 30 days?

    A. Precontemplation
    B. Contemplation
    C. Preparation
    D. Action

18. The objective, "By the end of this training, the participant will be able to filter a gallon of water and list five items to pack in an emergency kit," addresses:

    A. Knowledge and skills
    B. Attitudes and knowledge
    C. Skills and behavior
    D. Skills and attitudes

19. Immediately following a training, participants were given a post-test to assess knowledge. This represents what type of evaluation?

    A. Formative
    B. Process
    C. Outcome
    D. Summative

20. When developing trainings for adult learners, the most important principle for the instructor to keep in mind is:

    A. Make the training as easy as possible.
    B. Make the training relevant to the audience's jobs or personal lives.
    C. Be funny to keep the audience's attention.
    D. Explain your credentials for teaching so they will recognize your authority.

ANSWERS

1. D. Conclusions
"A theory is a set of interrelated concepts, definitions, and propositions that present a systematic view of events or situations by specifying relations among variables in order to explain and predict the events or situations" (Glanz, Lewis, & Rimer, 2002, p. 25).

2. C. Respect for individuals
Informed consent falls under the respect for individuals/autonomy pillar of the principles for ethical research.

3. C. Describe how you will measure variables in your study
Describing how you will measure variables in your study will be discussed in the methods section.

4. C. Decide which citations should be used for justifying your study
A reference manager can be a very helpful tool for organizing your work, but it cannot help you make decisions about what is valuable to your work.

5. C. Decisional balance
Decisional balance is a key construct of the Transtheoretical Model (TTM). It reflects that, at the beginning, the person is not adopting the new behavior because the either do not know about it, or the "cons" outweigh the "pros." As they learn more, the information they gain reduces the "cons" and increases the "pros," leading to a shift in attitude and behavior. By action, the "pros" outweigh the "cons."

6. D. Sending a congratulatory note for having made it through the first week
Conscious-raising information (like information or graphic videos) are used in the beginning of Transtheoretical Model (TTM) to move people from precontemplation to contemplation. Increasing people's perceptions of public support for the new behavior is a middle-stage approach. By the time a person is in action, we reinforce the new behavior in positive ways and help to manage stimuli that would lead to relapse in behaviors.

7. B. Perceived susceptibility
"Perceived susceptibility" is how likely a person thinks they are to be at risk from a particular health threat. "Perceived barriers" are those things which stand in the way of adopting the new behavior. Self-efficacy is

the confidence in being able to overcome barriers and perform the new behavior. A cue to action is the stimulus that triggers the new behavior.

8. C. Manual of Procedures

A Manual of Procedures, or MOP, is a document that contains policies, roles and responsibilities, procedures, and protocols for an implementation.

9. A. Individual

The Theory of Planned Behavior is an individual-level theory.

10. D. Identify determinants that lead people to problem behaviors and develop programs that are more likely to be successful in influencing the behavior

Theories help to identify the causes of the problem behaviors and guide the development of interventions that will then successfully intervene in the behavior.

11. B. Interventions that account for user's needs and preferences

Interventions that consider beneficiaries' needs and preferences are more likely to be successfully disseminated than ones that are not developed considering these aspects.

12. A. In the planning stages

Program sustainability must be considered from the beginning of the planning stages. If the program is not sustainable on its own, what partners or stakeholders can be brought in to help improve sustainability?

13. D. EBMR

Gantt chart, PERT (Program Evaluation and Review Technique), and CPM (Critical Path Method) are all methods of monitoring program implementation. EBMR (Evidence-Based Medicine Reviews) is a collection of databases that offer evidence-based programs such as the Cochrane Systematic Reviews.

14. B. Introduce the program to management, introduce the program to employees, do a health risk assessment, schedule trainings

First management, and then employees at large, need to know about the program before they are likely to buy into the idea of taking a health risk assessment. Once the results of the HRA are in hand, the health educator can begin scheduling trainings.

15. D. Selecting only one demographic group to serve for convenience of data collection

When project resources have to be rationed, care must be taken to do so in an ethical matter. Providing a wait-list, community referrals, and prioritizing needs are all ethical approaches if done thoughtfully and considered a priori. Selecting one demographic group for the convenience of the organization when there is high community demand is likely unethical.

16. C. Transtheoretical Model

The Transtheoretical Model posits that people move through stages in their way toward behavior change.

17. C. Preparation

In the Stages of Change model, people who are preparing to take action within the next 30 days are considered to be in Preparation.

18. A. Knowledge and skills

Filtering a gallon of water is a skill, but being able to list five items is a knowledge-level domain.

19. C. Outcome

A post-test measures the short-term outcome of the training—that is, what level of knowledge participants had after the training.

20. B. Make the training relevant to the audience's jobs or personal lives

Most adult learners respond well to a training when they can see that it has a tangible relevance to their lives either personally or professionally.

REFERENCES

Ajzen, I. (1991). The theory of planned behavior. *Organizational Behavior and Human Decision Processes, 50*(2), 179–211. doi:10.1016/0749-5978(91)90020-T

Ajzen, I., & Madden, T. J. (1986). Prediction of goal-driven behavior: Attitudes, intentions, and perceived behavioral control. *Journal of Experimental Social Psychology, 22*(5), 453–447. doi:10.1016/0022-1031(86)90045-4

Bandura, A. (2002). Social cognitive theory of mass communication. In J. Bryant, & M. B. Oliver (Eds.), *Media effects: Advances in theory and research* (pp. 94–124). New York, NY: Routledge.

Centers for Disease Control and Prevention National Prevention Information Network. (2015). *Cultural competence.* Retrieved from https://npin.cdc.gov/pages/cultural-competence#1

Fishbein, M., & Ajzen, I. (1975). *Belief, attitude, intention, and behavior: An introduction to theory and research.* Reading, MA: Addison-Wesley.

Glanz, K., Rimer, B. K., & Lewis, F. M. (Eds). (2002). *Health behavior and health education* (3rd ed.). San Francisco, CA: Jossey-Bass.

Health Research and Educational Trust. (2013, June). *Becoming a culturally competent health care organization.* Chicago, IL: Health Research & Educational Trust. Retrieved from www.hpoe.org.

Institute of Medicine. (2002). *Speaking of health: Assessing health communication strategies for diverse populations.* Washington, DC: National Academies Press. doi:10.17226/10018

McKenzie, J. F., Neiger, B. L, & Thackeray, R. (2016). *Planning, implementing, and evaluating health promotion programs: A primer* (7th ed.). Boston, MA: Pearson.

National Cancer Institute. (2002). *Making health communication programs work: A planner's guide.* Bethesda, MD: U.S. Department of Health and Human Services, Public Health Service, National Institutes of Health. Retrieved from https://www.cancer.gov/publications/health-communication/pink-book.pdf

Rogers, E. M. (1962). *Diffusion of innovation* (1st ed.). New York, NY: Free Press of Glencoe.

Chapter 5

Area IV: Conduct Evaluation and Research Related to Health Education/Promotion

INTRODUCTION

This chapter provides an overview of strategies and competencies needed to evaluate health education programs and interventions. **Evaluation** is the systematic investigation of the relevance, quality, worth, and/or significance of a health education program or intervention (Rychetnik, Hawe, Waters, Barratt, & Frommer, 2004; Scriven, 1998). Evaluation allows you to assign "value" to a program's efforts. Program evaluation often considers the merit (or quality) of a program or intervention (Donaldson & Lipsey, 2003). It also helps to define the worth (or value) of the program of intervention. For instance, sometimes evaluations focus on identifying the cost or the cost effectiveness of the program. Significance focuses on the impact or importance of a program or intervention for addressing the health problem.[1]

When developing an evaluation plan, health educators should ask themselves the following questions:

■ What will be evaluated (e.g., what are the outcome(s), problem(s), program(s), and context or environment)?

■ What aspects of the program should be considered when evaluating how well the program performs?

---

[1] NCHEC Competency 4.1. Develop evaluation plan for health education/promotion.

- What standards or targets must be reached for the program to be considered successful?

- What types of evidence will be used to determine how well the program worked?

- Are the conclusions about the program's performance justified and how do they compare to past evidence?

- How will the lessons learned from the evaluation be used to improve future programs and public health?

TYPES OF EVALUATION

Formative evaluation involves the use of data from the planning and implementation (i.e., process evaluation) to determine **fidelity**, or whether a program is being implemented in the way it was designed, and identifies ways to adjust how the program is being delivered (Rychetnik, Hawe, Waters, Barratt, & Frommer, 2004; Wholey, Hatry, & Newcomer, 2010).

Process evaluation is a way to monitor and describe the steps necessary for program implementation, and it can also aid in understanding the relationship between specific program elements and program outcomes (Saunders, Evans, & Joshi, 2005).

Process evaluations often help with determining fidelity (Bryant, Altpeter, & Whitelaw, 2006). Other questions that can be answered include the dose delivered and received, reach (e.g., participants or the extent to which the program was delivered to the intended audience), recruitment, and contextual factors (e.g., organizational issues and other barriers and facilitators.)

Summative evaluation examines how well the measures or judgments from the outcomes can be used to summarize and make conclusions about the program. It is often an important element of impact and outcome evaluations.

Impact evaluation refers to identifying the immediate or shorter-term effects of a program (Rychetnik et al., 2004). This might involve changes to knowledge, behavior, or attitudes. Often this phase of the evaluation focuses on how well the program did in achieving its short-term objectives.

Outcome evaluation involves measuring the overall outcomes and impacts of a program and measures the long-term outcomes, such as morbidity or mortality, after the program has been completed (Rychetnik et al., 2004).

DEVELOPING AN EVALUATION PLAN

It is important that health educators consider the best ways to evaluate the impact of their health education programs and interventions. There are several different frameworks that have been developed for such evaluations. While we will not cover all of them, health educators should be aware of some of the most commonly used frameworks in public health. These include the Centers for Disease Control and Prevention's (CDC's) Six-Step Framework for Program Evaluation; Reach, Effectiveness, Adoption, Implementation, and Maintenance (RE-AIM; Gaglio, Shoup, & Glasgow, 2013); and the Precede–Proceed Model (Green & Kreuter, 1999; please see Chapter 3). For the purpose of this chapter, we will focus only on the CDC's framework, given its wide use in evaluating health education and public health programs.

CDC's Six-Step Framework for Program Evaluation

The CDC's framework for evaluation involves a systematic, six-step process to guide and summarize essential elements for developing a program evaluation plan (Davis, 2006). This framework is often used by public health practitioners and health educators to guide program evaluations, and often it is required for evaluating the impact of CDC-funded programs. Thus, it is important that health educators become familiar with the six steps of this framework (Figure 5.1).

Figure 5.1 The Center for Disease Control and Prevention framework for evaluation.

Source: Centers for Disease Control and Prevention. (2017). A framework for program evaluation. Retrieved from https://www.cdc.gov/eval/framework

The six steps and primary activities (Koplan, Milstein, & Wetterhall, 1999) are:

1. **Engaging stakeholders** includes meeting with stakeholders to involve them in evaluation and gain consensus on the purpose of the evaluation.

2. **Describing the program** includes defining the mission, objectives, and key outcomes of the program.

3. **Focusing the evaluation design** includes the questions, data collection procedures, and protocols needed for the evaluation.

4. **Gathering credible evidence** includes collecting data, including defining indicators, to answer evaluation questions.

5. **Justifying conclusions** includes data analysis, summarization, and interpretation.

6. **Using and sharing lessons learned** includes reporting and presenting results of the evaluation and discussing with stakeholders how the results will be used for program improvement and future programs.

Logic Models

A logic model describes the sequence of events required to make a change by identifying the key program elements (Koplan et al., 1999). Elements that are connected within a logic model may vary but generally include:

- **Inputs/Resources:** Information and resources being used to develop or implement your program. These could include funding, staff, and stakeholders.

- **Activities:** The actions or changes being carried out to implement the program.

- **Outputs:** Results of the actions or changes, such as new policies, practices, or systems.

- **Outcomes:** Short-, intermediate-, and long-term changes in the target audience in such areas as behaviors, attitudes, knowledge, and disease rates (e.g., morbidity and mortality).

- **Indicators:** The specific, observable, and measurable characteristics of changes that demonstrate progress toward your outcomes or impact.

An example of a program logic model is shown in Figure 5.2.

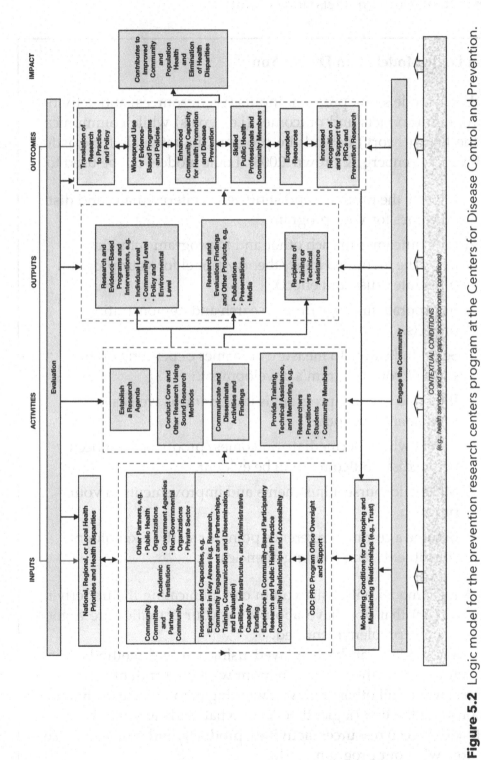

Figure 5.2 Logic model for the prevention research centers program at the Centers for Disease Control and Prevention.

Source: Retrieved from https://www.cdc.gov/prc/pdf/prc-logic-model.pdf

For examples of logic models and further details, please see www.cdc. gov/eval/tools/logic_models/index.html

---

What Logic Models Can Do For You

Logic models link program inputs (i.e., resources) and activities to program products and outcomes (i.e., goals) while communicating the logic (theory) behind the program, its rationale for existing (Gallivan, Greenberg, & Brown, 2008). Logic models can be used to:

1. Identify the products and short-term, intermediate, and distal outcomes for your program.

2. Link outcomes to each other and to program activities using the identified logic/theory/model for your program (illustrate cause and effect).

3. Incorporate findings from research and demonstration projects.

4. Select indicators to measure outcomes depending on the stage of your program's development.

5. Illustrate why the program is important, as well as its fundamental purpose.

6. Depict what intermediate outcomes/products must occur before distal outcomes will be evident.

7. Make midcourse adjustments and improvements in your program.

8. Become a common reference point for staff, stakeholders, constituents, and funding agencies.

A logic model will assist you in communicating the underlying theory (logic) that you have about why your activities are a good solution to the problem identified.

Logic models can be displayed using varying methods. Some read left to right; others, top to bottom with intermittent circles and squares; while still others follow a winding path. All are designed to demonstrate the link (logic/theory) of what leads to what. What are the links between resources, activities, products, and outcomes? Why and how will your program work?

(continued)

(continued)

> Logic models often provide the needed synthesis of your program to successfully convey why it is important, as well as the logic behind why you expect it to succeed. A logic model is an iterative tool, providing a framework to revisit throughout program planning, implementation, and evaluation.

Source: Centers for Disease Control and Prevention, 2017.

RESEARCH AND STUDY DESIGNS

Research plays an integral part in evidence-based public health and health education and promotion (CDC, 2006; CDC 2017). Depending on the purpose of your study or research, different research methods, such as quantitative, qualitative, or mixed methods, will be needed. We provide an overview of the key terms, methods, and research designs that are often used when conducting research as part of your health education programs in the following section.

KEY DEFINITIONS

Quantitative research is based on testing a hypothesis based on the concepts (variables) within a theory.

Qualitative research seeks to understand social phenomena through the exploration and interpretation of the meanings that people attach to, and use to make sense of, their experiences of the social world.

Sample size is the number of observations or participants in a study.

Data analysis involves analyzing data in some way to impose meaning.

Quantitative data analysis enables researchers to organize, interpret, and communicate numeric information.

Qualitative data analysis typically takes the narrative form in order to organize, provide structure, and elicit meaning, usually in the form of themes that emerged from coded data.

Problem statement describes the need for research or a program through the development of an argument.

Research question is a statement about the phenomenon that is being studied. Questions can be descriptive, relational, or causal.

Hypothesis is used to make a specific prediction about the answers to research questions. There are two approaches to conducting hypothesis testing: inductive reasoning (used to develop a hypothesis or theory) and deductive reasoning (used to test a theory or hypothesis).

Aims or objectives are used to specify accomplishments to be achieved by a study or program. Please see more in Chapter 3.

Validity refers to the degree to which something accurately represents a phenomenon.

Internal validity refers to research measurements reflecting the true intended concepts or when an intervention is delivered in the way it was designed. There are several threats to internal validity in research studies, such as *attrition* (loss of participants), *testing effects, history* (events outside the study that impact results), *instrumentation concerns*, and *maturation* (changes in subjects during the course of the study due to aging or other experiences unrelated to the study).

External validity represents findings being generalizable to other groups, settings, or contexts.

Measurement validity is the degree to which a measurement or tool accurately measures what it is designed to measure.

Reliability is the degree to which observations or measures can be replicated under the same conditions.

Variables are measured with numbers and analyzed with statistical procedures to determine whether predictive generalizations of a theory hold true.

Dependent variable is the outcome variable. An example of this might be measuring change in knowledge, attitudes, behaviors, or in a health condition, such as the risk of developing a disease or the severity of a disease.

Independent variables are often the variables you manipulate, measure, and/or record. For example, you might want to explore how physical activity level (dependent variable) differs by age and gender, or whether a health education program results in greater physical activity.

STUDY DESIGNS

Typically, health education and public health studies fall into two categories: observational (descriptive or analytical) or experimental studies (Rychetnik et al., 2004). Observational studies involve investigators collecting, recording, describing, and analyzing data on subjects and testing potential relationships. Observational studies do not involve the direct manipulation of a variable (Rychetnik, Frommer, Hawe, & Shiell, 2002). The types of study designs are cross-sectional (one point in time), ecological, cohort, case-control (retrospective), longitudinal (prospective), and hybrid.

Descriptive studies aim to identify the qualities or distribution of variables. Key components of descriptive studies are to:

- Examine phenomena as they naturally occur
- Describe levels or characteristics of several variables, or aspects of one variable
- Identify, when possible, an independent and a dependent variable
- Utilize quantitative data
- Often compare two populations
- Infrequently include generalization as a goal

Analytic studies focus on examining associations among the variables, and often this is based on testing a hypothesis about the relationship among the variables. These studies examine the association or relationship between two or more variables on a particular outcome (e.g., minutes of walking per day and weight loss). There is no manipulation of the independent variable. The researcher must be very careful about making any statements about cause and effect, given the observational nature of these types of studies. Prospective studies look at relationships over time; retrospective studies look at past occurrences.

Experimental studies differ from observational studies in that the investigator has direct control over the dependent variable (Thompson, Kegler, & Holtgrave, 2006). Moreover, experimental studies involve some type of intervention and control by the investigators; for instance, the study might be a clinical trial testing the effects of a drug or exercise protocol. Experimental studies aim to establish causality. There are two major types of experimental studies: randomized control trials (RCT or clinical trials) and community trials.

Quasi-experimental design includes controlled trials without randomization. They can have a comparison group or control group but participants would not be randomized to the intervention or control group. The limitations are that they cannot infer cause, variables are not controlled for, and there may be participant selection bias. Often these are more feasible for health education and community-based intervention studies.

Qualitative studies can include qualitative description, ethnography, grounded theory, and critical theory. For instance, a common data collection approach for qualitative research might involve participant observation, in-depth interviews, or focus groups. Often participants are selected based on convenience (nonprobability) or purposive (purposeful selection of specific individuals).

DATA COLLECTION, MANAGEMENT, AND ANALYSIS AND TYPES OF DATA[2]

Data collection and management are important tasks for health education specialists. Data can help you to determine how well your program worked and to identify areas that can be improved. It can also help with planning and effectiveness studies.

Health education specialists should ensure that data are collected in a structured manner. Both people collecting the data and the study participants are constrained to ensure quality and consistency in what is asked and how the answers are reported to maintain objectivity, reduce biases, and facilitate data analysis (CDC, 2017; Thompson et al., 2006). Data collection procedures are such that data are accurate, valid, and meaningful. It is also important to consider and identify existing instruments when evaluating outcomes, because often they have already been shown to be valid and reliable. Examples of existing data sources can include surveys such as the Behavioral Risk Factor Surveillance Survey (BRFSS) and the Youth Risk Behavioral Surveillance System (YRBSS), CDC's WONDER online database, or data on current online activities of older adults through the Pew Internet and American Life Project (pewinternet.org). Often health educators have to identify usable items from existing materials and use them as is, or adapt them to make them appropriate to a different population or to bring them up to date to modern usage or changing norms—adding Instagram to social media offerings, or updating demographic sections to provide choices more inclusive than simply "male" or "female," for instance.[3] When designing new instruments, it is important to think about reliability (precision) and validity (accuracy). Consider whether the tool is sensitive, specific, and appropriate to the objectives, can adequately capture the distribution of responses, and objectively measures the attribute or phenomenon.

---

[2] NCHEC Competency 4.2. Develop a research plan for health education/promotion; NCHEC Competency 4.4. Collect and manage data; NCHEC competency 4.5. Analyze data.

[3] NCHEC Competency 4.3. Select, adapt, and/or create instruments to collect data.

Types of Data

Nominal (categorical) data involves numbers used to classify characteristics into categories (e.g., gender, diagnosis, marital status, and race/ethnicity). Numbers serve as codes to represent these categories, and they have no quantitative meaning (e.g., 1 = female; 2 = male).

Ordinal (rank-order) data are used to sort people based on ranking of an attribute. For example, you might rank level of exercise intensity as 0 = sedentary; 1 = low; 2 = moderate; 3 = vigorous.

Interval (continuous) data can specify rank ordering on an attribute and assume equivalent distance between them, but its value does not indicate absolute magnitude (e.g., temperature, date of birth). There is equal distance between numbers on a scale, and data can be calculated meaningfully. Most clinical, social, and behavioral research instruments yield interval-level data.

Ratio data provide information on the intervals between objects, and the absolute magnitude of the attribute because they have a meaningful zero (e.g., weight, blood pressure, pulse rate).

Qualitative data include information from interviewing and observing study participants individually or as a group, as well as open-ended survey responses, documents, photographs, genealogies, maps, social network diagrams, diaries, journals, oral histories, and so on. The units of data collection include individuals and cultural systems. A longitudinal or cross-sectional length of time is utilized for data collection. Data are recorded using field notes, interview notes, observational notes, memos, logs, and recordings.

Data also need to be kept secure, and storage is often easier when utilizing an electronic database. Training in statistics will also be necessary when conducting quantitative data analysis, and many researchers use specific data analysis software programs.

Quantitative data analysis enables researchers to organize, interpret, and communicate numeric information. Researchers may also use descriptive or inferential statistics to test potential relationships among the variables. Qualitative data analysis typically uses narrative or other subjective accounts to organize and elicit meaning in the form of themes based on the coded data. Qualitative data analysis may involve content analysis, narrative analysis, discourse analysis, and grounded theory (Trochim, 2006).

LITERATURE REVIEW

A literature review is a critical component of planning for evaluations, including reviewing past work and evidence, selecting strategies that have been used successfully in the past, and identifying the need and potential outcomes. A literature review provides an in-depth analysis of recently published research findings (the state of the science) in an identified area. It is an analysis of what is known and what is missing (gaps) in the scientific literature. It provides a description of the state of the science and any existing gaps in a specifically identified area of interest. The literature review will inform the question or area of focus and guides the development of the evaluation plan.

A thorough literature review may identify evidence-based interventions that can be replicated, instruments that have been standardized and tested, procedures that can be adapted, and appropriate statistical tests and theoretical frameworks that can be used to guide the health education program or intervention and will support the evaluation plan.

There are several different types of literature reviews, and it is important to consider the scope of the review.

SCOPE OF THE LITERATURE REVIEW

When considering how comprehensive the review will be, it is important to think in terms of the time period for the literature identified and what types of evidence and past work should be used. It is sometimes suggested that the work completed or published in the past 10 years is ideal. However, it is important to include seminal work (e.g., studies and other work that may be older but has had a large influence on the field or topic area). Nevertheless, health educators should identify the literature that directly relates to the problem, the planned intervention and outcomes, and the strategies for evaluating how well the intervention does in addressing the problem.

Here are the types of literature that can be used in a literature review:

Theoretical literature includes conceptual models, theoretical frameworks, and evidence-based plans and methodologies. This literature provides a road map for ways to think about the problem and may help the health educator in identifying ways of explaining behavior or the causes of the problem.

Empirical literature includes research that has tested how theories apply to behavior or observed events. This involves research or past evaluation studies that tested a specific research question. This literature often describes the past literature, methods used to evaluate or test a hypothesis, and the results, and discusses how the research influences health education practice or future research. Sources of literature reviews include journals, books, theses and dissertations, conference proceedings, government reports, practice guidelines, citations, and websites.

Primary sources are reports of original findings that are published in peer-reviewed journals or scholarly books. Health educators should try to use primary sources whenever possible to ensure accuracy. Examples of primary sources are clinical trials, controlled trials, studies, and dissertations and theses.

Secondary sources include comments and synthesis, and often these articles summarize the findings from multiple original research studies on one topic. Examples of secondary sources are systematic reviews, meta-analyses, qualitative synthesis, review articles, and practice guidelines.

Systematic literature review is a method for identifying, interpreting, and synthesizing existing research evidence.

Meta-analyses involve a method of statistical synthesis that is used in some systematic reviews to quantitatively combine results from several studies, and then to summarize these findings.

INTERPRETING AND REPORTING ON EVALUATION RESULTS[4]

After you finish with data analysis, it important to be able to organize and interpret the results, justify conclusions, and then communicate the findings to stakeholders and the community (Koplan et al., 1999). In order to justify conclusions from a program evaluation, health educators need to understand the limits of their data and be able to defend the merit, worth, or significance of the findings. Conclusions should be linked to the findings, based on credible evidence, and consistent with the agreed-upon values or standards of stakeholders.

---

[4] NCHEC Competency 4.6. Interpret results; NCHEC Competency 4.7. Apply findings.

Reporting and dissemination can take different forms, such as written reports, presentations, peer-reviewed manuscripts, and public forums. This step is especially important because results may have an impact on decision making, policy, and future programs. Recommendations from a program evaluation will have an impact on continuing, expanding, revising, or ending a program based on the judgments made about the program's effectiveness. This is the way health education specialists incorporate evidence-based practices into the design, planning, implementation, and evaluation of health education programs and interventions. Tracking and sharing of lessons learned over the course of the evaluation are also important; they are essential to informed decision making around the future of health education programs.

CONCLUSION

This chapter provided an overview of strategies and competencies needed to successfully evaluate health education programs and interventions. It is important to consider the type of data (quantitative and qualitative) you will collect, how you will manage and analyze the data, and how you will prepare for the reporting and dissemination of the findings. What you learned in this chapter about evaluation is critical for ensuring the success of health education programs. In Chapter 6 you will review Area V: Administer and Manage Health Education/Promotion.

REVIEW QUESTIONS

1. In evaluation research, experiments with control groups:
   - **A.** Provide the clearest evidence of a causal association
   - **B.** Use the same intervention with both groups, to double the evidence
   - **C.** Always place participants in groups by random assignment
   - **D.** Are not suitable for use in public health

2. An outcomes evaluation of a program requires all of the following, EXCEPT:
   - **A.** Uncertainty about the effect of the program
   - **B.** A program with a logic model
   - **C.** An intervention that is clearly defined
   - **D.** A program with a theory or rationale of why it works

3. Community-based participatory research challenges all of these Positivist tenets EXCEPT:

   A. Science is neutral and value free.
   B. There is one valid way of interpreting reality.
   C. Research needs a systematic approach and clear disclosure of the methods used.
   D. Because of their training, scientists are the real experts and their opinion carries more weight than that of community members.

4. For the dissemination of research findings to be effective, it is necessary that

   A. The research occurs in a neutral location
   B. They be presented once, to minimize miscommunication
   C. The intended audience is able to access the findings
   D. The findings are presented in a way that is convenient for the researchers

5. Which is NOT true of publishing research or program findings?

   A. May contribute to future funding
   B. Delays other research being done
   C. Is crucial to career advancement
   D. Makes it possible for other researchers to use the results

6. A local health department develops a program including health education and screening to reduce the number of cases of gonorrhea in the county a year. A measure of the program's outcomes would be:

   A. The number of office visits for treatment of gonorrhea
   B. The number of public service announcements (PSAs) aired on the radio
   C. The number of gonorrhea cases after the campaign
   D. The number of people who could name the signs and symptoms of gonorrhea

7. Which of the following is NOT a common threat to internal validity?

   A. History effects
   B. Maturation effects
   C. Selection effect
   D. Hawthorne effect

8. All of the following correctly describe the characteristics of triangulations EXCEPT:

   A. Triangulation means using three sets of data in studying a topic or setting.
   B. Triangulation may involve contextualizing the information gathered.
   C. Triangulation may involve using more than one methodological approach.
   D. Triangulation is used to establish validity in qualitative research.

9. An evaluator finds a statistically significant relationship between variable X and variable Y at the 0.05 level. What does this mean?

   A. Ninety-five times out of 100, the results are true.
   B. There is a 5% chance the results are true.
   C. A person could be 90% sure that the results of the study were a reflection of the relationship in the population if random sampling was used.
   D. If 100 samples were drawn, results like these would be obtained by chance 95% of the time.

10. Which of the following is NOT true?

    A. One study, no matter how well designed or implemented or how large the sample, can provide the definitive evidence of validity.
    B. Reliability is necessary for validity to exist.
    C. A measure that has been repeatedly shown to be valid for population A and B will be valid for population C.
    D. Reliability refers to how consistent the test is at returning the same result when the same results are entered.

11. Which of the following is true?

    A. Reliability is a precondition to validity.
    B. Validity is a precondition to reliability.
    C. As validity increases, often reliability decreases.
    D. While reliability addresses error, validity addresses confidence.

12. Which of the following is not a potential disadvantage of telephone-based interviewing?

    A. Lower cost per person than in-person interviews
    B. Random sampling of the general population
    C. The interviewer's ability to interpret responses
    D. Ability to ask personal or sensitive questions

13. Which of the following is false?

    A. Reliability reduces random error.
    B. Validity reduces bias.
    C. Well-designed studies use measures that yield no error.
    D. If researchers average random errors over many measurements, theoretically there should be zero errors as a result.

14. Which section of a journal article presents the steps the authors took to carry out the intervention or experiment?

    A. Overview
    B. Methods
    C. Results
    D. Discussion

15. According to the Centers for Disease Control and Prevention's Framework for Program Evaluation, ensuring that an evaluation will be conducted "legally, ethically, and with due regard for the welfare of those involved in the evaluation, as well as those affected by its results" is acting with which standard for effective evaluation?

    A. Utility
    B. Feasibility
    C. Propriety
    D. Accuracy

16. What is an advantage of using electronic tablets to collect data in an evaluation?

    A. Survey development is easier
    B. It reduces the need for data entry
    C. Tablet technology is "one-size-fits-all"
    D. It eliminates data management issues

17. A health educator is preparing a report for a funder on an injury-reduction program in an interstate repaving work zone. He is planning on reporting on the number of sessions he held with workers educating them on the proper ways to wear personal protective equipment (PPE) and the topics covered in those sessions. This would be part of his:

    A. Formative evaluation
    B. Process evaluation

  C. Impact evaluation
  D. Outcome evaluation

18. A health educator is tasked with preventing death from house fires. She decides to focus on educating elementary schoolchildren and senior citizens on the risks of house fires and proper evacuation techniques, and to distribute smoke detectors through the schools and at community events. If she conducted a short survey after the event at a senior center to ask if the seniors liked the event, understood the materials she presented, and planned to install the smoke detectors, that would be an example of what kind of evaluation, according to the PRECEDE–PROCEED model?

  A. Formative evaluation
  B. Process evaluation
  C. Impact evaluation
  D. Outcome evaluation

19. A health educator has been hired to develop an after-school program for a large school district in an urban/suburban area that contains a mix of high- and low-income neighborhoods. There is a small budget for needs assessment. What would be the best method to ensure he has the most representative data to plan for the needs of the families when developing his program?

  A. Nominal group process
  B. Delphi panel
  C. Focus groups
  D. Surveys

20. A logic model can help to answer the following questions, EXCEPT:

  A. Where is the program going?
  B. How will the program get there?
  C. Who is responsible for implementation activities?
  D. How will the program know if it has been successful?

ANSWERS

1. A. Provide the clearest evidence of a causal association

While not always feasible in evaluations, a control group provides evidence about whether a particular program caused the change that is being seen.

2. B. A program with a logic model

To conduct an evaluation, you need a clearly defined intervention with a theory or rationale for why it works and the desire to understand the effect of the program. A logic model is a helpful planning and implementation tool, but it is not required; many evaluators, however, would develop one during the evaluation if one did not already exist.

3. C. Research needs a systematic approach and clear disclosure of the methods used

Regardless of the approach used, research must have a systematic approach and disclose the methods being used to conduct the research.

4. C. The intended audience is able to access the findings

For dissemination to happen effectively, the research or program findings must be distributed in places and ways that are accessible to the intended audience(s).

5. B. Delays other research being done

Publishing your findings does not delay future work from being conducted; it is a crucial part of the work you are doing. Whether those findings are published in the peer-reviewed literature, posted on your organization's website, or presented at local conferences or "take-back" sessions to the community—whatever the appropriate method of dissemination, that work is part of the research/program development process.

6. C. The number of gonorrhea cases after the campaign

In this case, reducing the number of people who have gonorrhea was the goal of the program, so that would be the outcome measure researched. The number of PSAs aired would be a process measure, and the number of office visits and number of people who could name the signs/symptoms of gonorrhea would be impact or short-term outcomes that help you reach your long-term goal of a reduction in cases.

7. D. Hawthorne effect

The Hawthorne effect is a threat to external validity. It refers to the positive reaction participants may experience just because they receive any treatment. We cannot generalize from the results if we cannot ascertain that it was specifically and exclusively the treatment that caused the difference. Administering another treatment for the control group helps solve this problem (this is called placebo or standard treatment). The other answers listed are threats to internal validity.

8. A. Triangulation means using three sets of data in studying a topic or setting

Triangulation means exploring multiple points of views and perspectives in a given setting, establishing relationships between these perspectives, and integrating them into the analysis of findings. In a broader research context, triangulation may also involve employing multiple and differing methodological approaches and methodologies, different sources of information, and differing theoretical approaches. However, these multiple, differing perspectives, approaches, and sources do not have an established number, and certainly do not have to be exactly three.

9. A. Ninety-five times out of 100, the results are true

A statistically significant relationship at the level of 0.05 means that 95 times out of a 100, the results are a true reflection of what is happening in the population. Another way of saying it is that there is a 5% chance that the results are observed due to chance alone.

10. C. A measure that has been repeatedly shown to be valid for population A and B will be valid for population C

Measures can be valid, or measure what they are supposed to measure, for one (or multiple) population(s), but not for another. This validity is demonstrated over a series of studies.

11. A. Reliability is a precondition to validity

Your measure has to reliably measure what it measures before it can be valid. That is, if you get on a scale 10 times, the same number has to appear each time before we can confidently report your weight.

12. A. Lower cost per person than in-person interviews

Telephone-based interviewing has many potential benefits for evaluation, but also comes with some potential disadvantages, especially for the general public. Response rates tend to be fairly low, and sampling frames leave out those without phones, or—depending on the frame—may only include those with landlines. On the phone, visual cues are lost, as is the ability to share visual aids, and people are often loath to share personal information without the kind of rapport that can be built in an in-person interview. On the plus side, such interviews are relatively inexpensive to conduct, allowing for substantial amounts of data to be generated at a relatively low unit cost.

13. C. Well-designed studies use measures that yield no error

No measure or technique yet invented has inherent zero error. We select a priori how much error we are willing to accept in our measurement and interpret our results in light of those assumptions.

14. B. Methods

The Methods (or Methodology) section describes the actions undertaken by the authors or research team to conduct the intervention or research.

15. C. Propriety

The CDC's Framework for Program Evaluation can be retrieved from www.cdc.gov/eval/framework/index.htm.

16. B. It reduces the need for data entry

Tablets can be a great choice for collecting data and completing data entry at the same time in the field. You are essentially getting your participants (or your research or intervention staff) to complete data entry at the time of the interview. However, by using the tablet, you often need complicated skip patterns and must choose from a constantly changing range of hardware and software. And though using tablets reduces your need for data entry, data management issues remain, including data cleaning, analysis, and reporting.

17. B. Process evaluation

Process evaluation determines whether program activities were implemented as they were planned.

18. C. Impact evaluation

According to PRECEDE–PROCEED, immediate- or short-term effects of a program are measured by impact evaluation. Some evaluation models or schools of thought view impact evaluation as looking at the final (most distal) results from an intervention.

19. D. Surveys

Although a mixed-methods approach would probably be best, in this case, surveys would be your best answer. Neither a nominal group process nor a Delphi panel is appropriate here. Focus groups would provide interesting information, but given the disparate needs of urban and suburban populations and high- and low-income families for after-school care and the small budget for needs assessment, a survey is going to be the best option.

20. C. Who is responsible for implementation activities?

Logic models answer the "big questions" about a program—where is it going, how will it get there, what will show that it has arrived. Specific details, such as who is responsible for implementing specific activities, are not generally shown on a logic model—such information is more likely found on a Gantt chart or other monitoring document.

REFERENCES

Bryant, L. L., Altpeter, M., & Whitelaw, N. A. (2006). Evaluation of health promotion programs for older adults: An introduction. *Journal of Applied Gerontology, 25*(3), 197–213. doi:10.1177/0733464806288562

Centers for Disease Control and Prevention. (2006). *Principles of epidemiology in public health practice* (3rd ed.). Atlanta, GA: Centers for Disease Control and Prevention. Retrieved from https://www.cdc.gov/ophss/csels/dsepd/ss1978/ss1978.pdf

Centers for Disease Control and Prevention. (2017). *Step 2B: Logic models.* Retrieved from https://www.cdc.gov/oralhealth/state_programs/pdf/logic_models.pdf

Davis, M. V. (2006). Teaching practical public health evaluation methods. *American Journal of Evaluation, 27*(2), 247–256. doi:10.1177/0198214006286422

Donaldson, S., & Lipsey, M. (2003). Roles for theory in contemporary evaluation practice: Developing practical knowledge, evaluating social programs and problems. *Visions for the New Millennium, 3*(3), 111–142.

Gaglio, B., Shoup, J. A., & Glasgow, R. E. (2013). The RE-AIM framework: A systematic review of use over time. *American Journal of Public Health, 103*(6), e38–e46. doi:10.2105/ajph.2013.301299

Gallivan, J., Greenberg, R., & Brown, C. (2008). The National Diabetes Education Program evaluation framework: How to design an evaluation of a multifaceted public health education program. *Preventing Chronic Disease, 5*(4), 1–8. Retrieved from https://www.ncbi.nlm.nih.gov/pmc/articles/PMC2578767

Green, L. W., & Kreuter, M. W. (1999). The precede–proceed model. In *Health promotion planning: An educational approach* (3rd ed., pp. 32–43). Mountain View, CA: Mayfield Publishing.

Koplan, J. P., Milstein, R. L., & Wetterhall, S. (1999). *Framework for program evaluation in public health.* Atlanta, GA: U.S. Department of Health & Human Services.

Rychetnik, L., Frommer, M., Hawe, P., & Shiell, A. (2002). Criteria for evaluating evidence on public health interventions. *Journal of Epidemiology and Community Health, 56*(2), 119–127. doi:10.1136/jech.56.2.119

Rychetnik, L., Hawe, P., Waters, E., Barratt, A., & Frommer, M. (2004). A glossary for evidence-based public health. *Journal of Epidemiology and Community Health, 58*(7), 538–545. doi:10.1136/jech.2003.011585

Saunders, R. P., Evans, M. H., & Joshi, P. (2005). Developing a process-evaluation plan for assessing health promotion program implementation: A how-to guide. *Health Promotion Practice, 6*(2), 134–147. doi:10.1177/1524839904273387

Scriven, M. (1998). A minimalist theory of evaluation: The least theory that practice requires. *American Journal of Evaluation, 19*(1), 57–70. doi:10.1177/109821409801900105

Thompson, N., Kegler, M., & Holtgrave, D. (2006). Program evaluation. In R. Crosby, R. DiClemente, & L. Salazar (Eds.), *Research methods in health promotion* (pp. 199–225). San Francisco, CA: Jossey-Bass.

Trochim, W. M. (2006). *The research methods knowledge base* (2nd ed.). Retrieved from http://www.socialresearchmethods.net/kb/unitanal.php

Wholey, J. S., Hatry, H. P., & Newcomer, K. E. (2010). *Handbook of practical program evaluation.* San Francisco, CA: Jossey-Bass.

Chapter 6

Area V: Administer and Manage Health Education/Promotion

INTRODUCTION

This chapter provides an overview of tools and strategies used by health educators to administer and manage health education and/or promotion programs. It will include a discussion of budgets, timelines, human resource management, and professional and leadership development.

MANAGE FISCAL RESOURCES[1]

Finding Fiscal and Other Resources

Health educators should be aware of the different grants, contracts, and other fiscal resources available to support health education programs. Common sources of funding include federal, state, county, city, and local funds. Often the various sources of funding have rolling cycles for applications.

There are several search engines available to identify the range of sources of funding available to support health education programs. Following are a few examples of commonly used websites:

http://fundingopps.cos.com—Provides a list of more than 15,000 international funding sources.

---

[1] NCHEC Competency 5.1. Manage financial resources for health education/promotion programs.

http://grants.nih.gov/grants/guide—This is the key place for finding grants from the National Institutes of Health (NIH).

www.grants.gov—The leading source of information on grants from the federal government including NIH, the Centers for Disease Control and Prevention (CDC), Health Resources and Services Administration (HRSA), National Science Foundation (NSF), Department of Defense (DoD), and Food and Drug Administration (FDA).

Prepare Requests/Proposals to Obtain Fiscal Resources

Health educators are often responsible for preparing letters of intent and proposal in order to fund their programs and staff.

Writing a Compelling Letter of Intent

Many foundations require a letter of intent or inquiry prior to allowing you to submit a proposal. Often the requirements or areas that should be addressed are highlighted in the application process. The following broad areas should be considered when writing a letter of intent:

- Title
- Introduction
- Problem/need statement
- Literature review
- Goals and objectives of the project
- Brief project description
- Evaluation approach/research design
- Plans for sustainability
- Costs or overall budget

Key Elements of Proposals

- Project Summary/Abstract
- Research/Project Plan
    - Specific aims, goals, and objectives
    - Significance

- Innovation
- Approach
- Budget and Justification
- Letters of Support (LOS)

Tips for Writing your Proposal

- Start planning early
- Read the application instructions carefully
- Use language that can be easily understood by reviewers, scientists, and the public
- Use language that grabs the reader
- Emphasize the long-term objectives and impact
- Conduct a literature review
- Include findings from prior studies and projects
- Create a well-organized and easily readable application

Also see https://grants.nih.gov/grants/grant_tips.htm for additional resources.

DEVELOP BUDGETS TO SUPPORT HEALTH EDUCATION/PROMOTION EFFORTS

Health educators are often responsible for developing and managing program budgets and reporting. A **budget** is a document that demonstrates how much money is necessary to deliver program activities and fulfill program objectives (Macdowall, Bonnell, & Davies, 2006). When developing a budget for a proposal, it is important to know about allowable costs. Also look into allowable direct and indirect costs. **Direct costs** are those directly attributable to your program's outputs, and generally include personnel costs (salary and benefits) as well as other costs of products and services necessary to provide the program. **Indirect costs**, often called "overhead," are the expenses organizations pay that are not related to any one project's outputs. Examples include utilities, rent, and depreciation. Organizations often calculate indirect costs as a percentage of direct costs; funders may have a maximum amount they allow for indirect costs. Health education specialists need to be able to develop and implement systems and procedures to monitor the use of funds and oversee health education program budgets. While budget and finance departments often oversee expenditures and budget monitoring, health education specialists will likely have some role in planning and budget monitoring.

It is important to establish systems for monitoring the use of funds and prepare fiscal reports that will be shared with funding agencies. It is imperative that requirements, guidelines, and policies are reviewed prior to use of funds. In addition, systems for tracking the budget will be needed. Health education specialists should also include reporting requirements and their due dates in overall program planning. Demonstrating ethical behavior in managing fiscal resources is also important for health education specialists. It may also be helpful to utilize conduct cost-effective analyses (Graham, Corso, Morris, Segui-Gomez, & Weinstein, 1998). Understanding the costs and benefits of health education programs and strategies will be important for guiding future plans and sustainability of health education programs.

As mentioned in Chapter 5, data collection and management are important tasks for health education specialists. Data are necessary for determining how well the program worked and identifying areas for improvement. Data are also necessary for determining cost-effectiveness and sustainability plans.

Often, a health education specialist may be responsible for writing reports on the project's progress and supplying these reports to funders and other stakeholders. Detail and accuracy in reporting are necessary in order to demonstrate accountability for the program's accomplishments, expenses, and lessons learned. It is important to develop skills in the synthesis and analysis of data for reporting. Often, health educators require skills in various areas such as data analysis, evaluation, accounting, program management, human resources, and public relations.

Timelines are also important for managing budgets and health education program activities and goals. Logic models are often used to represent timelines for health program activities and goals. However, it is also important to develop a timeline for budgets and reporting.

OBTAIN ACCEPTANCE AND SUPPORT FOR PROGRAMS

Health educators should make sure to use effective communication strategies to obtain program support (Caburnay, Kreuter, & Donlin, 2001). For instance, it may be useful to hold a press conference and/

or develop relationships with the media to ensure public awareness of your health education programs and services. Communication strategies should also consider the community and relevant stakeholders. As mentioned in Chapter 3, it is also important to involve stakeholders in management strategies and efforts to sustain health education programs (Macdowall et al., 2006). Stakeholders include primary (e.g., potential beneficiaries of the program), secondary (e.g., those involved in the programs delivery), and key stakeholders (e.g., those vital for program delivery and maintenance).

Encouraging Professional Development

It is also important to provide support for staff and to encourage professional development. Professional development opportunities may include academic coursework, management training, attendance at national conferences, continuing education trainings and seminars, and other opportunities identified by leadership or staff. More about this is described later in this chapter in the section, Manage Human Resources, and in Chapter 10.

Explain How Program Goals Align with Organizational Structure, Mission, and Goals

Health educators often support their organizations' overall vision and help to explain their mission and long-term goals. They often have to convey the mission and objectives of the program to participants, stakeholders, community members, funders, and policymakers. Logic models can help to summarize a health education program's overall goals, objectives, and mission. Please see Chapter 5 for more details about logic models.

Strategic Planning

According to the CDC (n.d.), **strategic planning** is a practical process to help the organizations to adapt products, services, and activities of the needs of the populations your program serves. Strategic plans can help improve organizational performance, use of resources, decision making, stakeholder communication, and political support for your program.

Strategic plans seek to answer the following questions: *Where are we now? Where do we want to be? How do we get there?*

Strategic planning consists of six steps[2]:

1. **Prepare**—Establish the purpose, create a planning group, and identify the needed data.

2. **Assess**—Analyze internal and external environment by conducting strengths, weaknesses, opportunities, threats (SWOT) analysis (see the following section).

3. **Create** (a 5-year plan)—Prioritize strategies; revise logic model; and develop annual work plan, communication, implementation, and evaluation processes.

4. **Communicate**—Share the plan with key stakeholders.

5. **Implement**—Implement the processes and work plans.

6. **Evaluate**—Summarize the overall processes and challenges based on annual evaluation data.

Organizational Assessments and Situational Analysis

The context in which programs operate or will operate should be peri-odically assessed. A SWOT analysis examines the internal and external, as well as positive and negative factors, in addition to the ethical impli-cations of a particular intervention. **Strengths** are things that are positive and internal, or under control of the program planners. **Weaknesses** are negative things that are known quantities about a program. For example, a weakness of using TV commercials to get people to quit smoking is that it is very expensive and you have to run a lot of commercials to get even a few people to think about quitting smoking. **Opportunities** are things that are positive, but outside of a program. If a celebrity becomes ill with a disease, that (sadly) can be an opportunity for your program. National attention around a disease seasonally, such as in October for breast cancer, is another example of an opportunity. Finally, **threats** are both negative and outside of your control. Cuts to funding, national dis-asters, clinical trial failures, scandals, and competition are all examples of threats.

Exhibit 6.1 is an example of a completed SWOT analysis from CDCynergy.

---

[2] NCHEC Competency 5.4. Gain acceptance and support for health education/promotion programs.

Exhibit 6.1 Sample SWOT analysis from CDCynergy School Physical Activity Intervention

Strengths	Weaknesses
■ Easy access and wide reach to teens ■ Schools offer centralized communication and structure ■ Heart Healthy already had established ties with schools throughout the state ■ Many studies show that health education in schools reduces the prevalence of health risk behaviors among young people. (CDC's School Health Programs At-A-Glance 2000 www.cdc.gov/nccdphp/dash/ataglanc.htm) ■ Two-part intervention (peer advocate model and communications campaign) ■ Teachers, food service personnel, and athletic directors can contribute their expertise	■ Home or family norms (identified by teens as key influences on teen diets and levels of physical activity) cannot be easily targeted ■ Potential lack of school support and commitment to program can weaken program effectiveness ■ Physical activity and nutrition are not considered "academic" and may not have high priorities on high school campuses ■ Not all campuses have adequate and safe facilities to provide proper eating, physical education, and physical activity areas ■ Reliance on teens to set standards of behavior for each other may be tenuous
Opportunities	**Threats**
■ Changes in policy and/or environment may effect long-term change ■ Communications campaign based on feedback from "early adopter" teens may widen program reach ■ Funding was available to work with high schools participating in a United States Department of Agriculture program for underserved students ■ School programs can help youth establish lifelong patterns of healthy behaviors ■ Schools provide a setting where teens can practice healthy behaviors ■ Healthy eating is considered "in"; target audience may be more receptive to program messages ■ Because schools do not have adequate funding to provide nutrition education and physical activity and education programs, new programs developed and implemented by outside agencies can provide tremendous assistance to schools	■ Sensitivity to multicultural and underserved youth is necessary ■ May confront resistance by parents and schools in their roles as "gatekeepers" of information toward minors if they do not agree with or understand the importance of program's goals and messages ■ Attempts to change school policy or environment can become political (raises budgetary and funding issues) ■ Schools and persons may be put into a negative light if program shows that schools are not supporting policy and environmental changes that support program goals ■ Challenge exists to obtain program buy-in by teachers and school administrators

(continued)

Exhibit 6.1 Sample SWOT analysis from CDCynergy School Physical Activity Intervention *(continued)*

Opportunities	Threats
■ Opportunity to build relationships between schools and community organizations around public health issues	■ Resistance to menu changes for healthier foods from vending-machine companies and other food service providers, because such changes might result in loss of business or income for them.

Source: Centers for Disease Control and Prevention, & Oak Ridge Institute for Science and Education. (2002). *CDCynergy web: Your guide to successful health communication.* Retrieved from https://www.orau.gov/cdcynergy/web/default.htm.

CDC, Centers for Disease Control and Prevention; SWOT, strengths, weaknesses, opportunities, threats.

DEMONSTRATE LEADERSHIP[3]

Health educators often take on leadership roles. The national Public Health Education Leadership Institute (PHELI) has developed a competency framework for health educators' leadership development (Wright et al., 2003). It focuses on conceptual development, building skills, refining them based on feedback, and personal development. The key leadership competencies include the following:

■ Visionary leadership—Health educators lead by developing, articulating, encouraging, facilitating, and supporting others to understand and share the program or organization's vision.

■ Sense of mission—Health educators must also be able to identify, articulate, and translate an understanding of the mission, vision, professional values, beliefs, and ethics.

■ Effective change agent—Health educators are responsible for driving change through learning, assessment, analysis, strategic planning, innovation, development, implementation, being a role model, taking risks, empowering others, and evaluation.

---

[3] NCHEC Competency 5.5. Demonstate leadership.

- An understanding of political realities—Health educators should be aware of the political process, policy analysis, translating policy into action, and crisis negotiation.

- An understanding of transorganizational competencies—Health educators should have an understanding of the organizations dynamics, interorganizational collaboration mechanisms, and social marketing.

- An understanding of team leadership competencies—Health educators should acquire skills in team building, facilitation, cultural sensitivity and competency, feedback methods, mediation, negotiation, coaching, and motivational interviewing (reflective listening, objective feedback, avoiding arguments, rolling with resistance, and supporting self-efficacy). (Wright et al., 2000).

MANAGE HUMAN RESOURCES[4]

Engaging volunteers is one way to support community partnerships, encourage sustainability, and obtain community support for health education programs. Volunteers can help to support your health education programs by developing rapport with community members, delivering health education trainings, and identifying, recruiting, and training additional trustworthy community members to volunteer (Merzel, & D'Afflitti, 2003). Internships for undergraduate and graduate students is another way to support health education programs and contribute to the training of the future health education workforce.

Volunteers provide many positive traits: no-cost labor, potential sources of funding, networking opportunities, and the potential to gain access to populations otherwise not accessible to the organization. However, volunteers also have needs and require investments from the organization in the form of recruitment, retention, training, and the development and enforcement of policies and procedures.

Professional development and training are also an important area to consider for health education workforce including staff and volunteers. In addition, succession planning and the development of staff are important for sustaining health education programs. There are several strategies that can be used to enhance the health education workforce (Novick & Mays,

---

[4] NCHEC Competency 5.6. Manage human resources.

2005). This includes graduate education such as an MPH or Masters in Health Education. Regular training is also needed for the health education workforce. This includes on-the-job training, leadership and skills-based training, and career development. Major areas to consider for on-the-job and skills-based training include assessment and epidemiology, analysis and critical thinking, effective skills in communication, grant writing, program evaluation and development, policy development and advocacy, and organizational leadership (Novick & Mays, 2005).

A Word on Technology[5]

One of the tasks a health educator must be able to do is to manage and integrate technology into health education and promotion in ways that makes working, partnering, and collaborating easier and more efficient, and means bringing ethical, effective materials to the most number of people. Today, more than ever, technology has the promise of bringing high-quality health education materials to people in ways that were barely imaginable even a few decades in the past—text reminders of appointments for pregnant women or video content delivered daily via social media have become so commonplace we forget how new and extraordinary they would seem to health educators a generation ago. However, headlines also remind us that data breaches and privacy concerns go hand in hand with these technologies, and we have responsibilities to make sure that we are employing technologies in ways that are ethical and protect participants. Likewise, health educators must constantly be assessing participant comfort with technology and the appropriateness of using technology with different populations and ensure that technology does not exclude participation due to disability, reading level, comfort level, or access. While the "digital divide" has narrowed over time, significant gaps continue to occur, especially in populations of color, those older than 65 years, people of lower socioeconomic status (SES), and those living in rural areas. While sometimes it seems like a job in and of itself to keep up with the changes in technology, resources like the Pew Internet and American Life Project (www.pewinternet.org), which tracks the habits and activities of Americans online, and leading health communication journals, such as the *Journal of Health Communication*, *Health Communication*, *Health Education & Behavior*, and *Health Promotion Practice* (to name just a few), can be great sources of information of how others are using technology effectively.

---

[5] NCHEC Competency 5.2. Manage technology resources.

FACILITATE PARTNERSHIPS IN SUPPORT OF HEALTH EDUCATION[6]

Health education specialists need to dedicate time to the development and maintenance of partnerships. Key areas to consider include (Israel, Schulz, Parker, & Becker, 1998): trust and respect; equitable distribution of power and control; planning for and addressing differences in perspectives, priorities, values, beliefs, and language; transparency in funding and budgets; communication around tasks and priorities; developing and ensuring time efficient processes; evaluating the partnership; and considering the feasibility of sustaining partnerships.

Key terms (Royeen, Jensen, & Harvan, 2011) for partnerships and collaboration include the following:

Interdisciplinary: across multiple disciplines

Interprofessional: across multiple professions

Multidisciplinary: includes many disciplines

Shared leadership: driving change in a collaborative manner

Collaboration: working, thinking, and taking action together

Memorandum of Understanding (MOU): a broad document indicating common interests and intended actions, but not specific or legally enforceable

Memorandum of Agreement (MOA): a document specifying work on a specific project that has been agreed upon and outlining terms and responsibilities of each partner (also known as a **cooperative agreement**)

CONCLUSION

This chapter covered tips and strategies for administering and managing health education programs. It highlighted the importance of developing budgets, timelines, reporting strategies, workforce and leadership development, and human resource management. In Chapter 7, Area VI: Serve as a Health Education/Promotion Resource Person, we will discuss how health educators can serve as the resource to the public and community members about a range of public health topics.

---

[6] NCHEC Competency 5.3. Manage relationships with partners and other stakeholders.

REVIEW QUESTIONS

1. Which of the following U.S. federal laws prohibits the sharing of most individually identifiable health information without prior authorization from an individual?

   A. National Labor Relations Act
   B. Americans with Disabilities Act
   C. Health Insurance Portability and Accountability Act
   D. Occupational Safety and Health Act

2. An organization needs volunteers to help staff in a health clinic in an underserved area. What would be the first step in planning a recruitment campaign?

   A. Develop a website where volunteers could log their hours
   B. Schedule a training for new volunteers
   C. Create job descriptions for the volunteer positions
   D. Use social media to help identify interested volunteers

3. Which of the following is the least helpful function of a program budget?

   A. Planning
   B. Monitoring
   C. Motivating
   D. Decision making

4. The dominant paradigm of health in the United States is built upon a set of shared meanings through which health is understood. Which of the following is not a characteristic of a dominant paradigm of health?

   A. The kinds of questions that are asked
   B. The methodology typically used to answer the questions
   C. The ways in which studies are conducted and written
   D. Who is included in an institutional review board (IRB) review panel

5. Before approving a strategic plan, it is important to receive feedback and acceptance from whom?

   A. The organization's management and staff
   B. Key stakeholders
   C. A and B
   D. All related social service organizations in the area

6. When hiring new employees, a health educator should never inquire about which of the following during the interview process?

   A. The candidate's education and experience
   B. Any challenges or difficulties the candidate has experienced in the past
   C. The candidate's childcare arrangements
   D. The learning style the candidate prefers

7. Checking references when hiring a job candidate is critical because it allows you:

   A. To be sure you have hired the right person
   B. To understand how they functioned in their past employment, educational, or volunteer experience
   C. To tell if their last work place environment is comparable to yours
   D. To avoid confirming the candidate's educational credentials

SCENARIO for QUESTIONS 8 to 10: A community-based food bank in a large, urban area recognizes a large proportion of its clients are at high risk for diabetes. They develop partnerships with local Federally Qualified Health Care Centers (FQHCs), and a community-based Diabetes Prevention Program, which is an evidence-based practice for preventing or delaying the onset of diabetes in high-risk people. They begin screening clients who use the food bank for their risk of prediabetes, and when clients score above the level of concern, they are referred to healthcare, and, if the client wishes, are referred—for no-cost—to health coaches. They are also given food at the food bank that is appropriate for people with diabetes—that is, low-sugar foods, fresh produce, whole grains, and lean meats. They are also partnering with a technology company to ensure that text messages go out to food bank clients to alert them of food pickups, and deliver health education messages promoting healthy eating and physical activity. Answer the following questions based on this scenario:

8. After identifying the need for intervening in the population, the food bank sought financial support to help fund their efforts. Which of the following would have been the least helpful place to seek funding for their project:

   A. Grants.gov
   B. Feeding America

C. Clinicaltrials.gov

D. Local foundations

9. In generating referrals to healthcare clinics and Diabetes Prevention Programs, which ethical principle is the program following by ensuring that the program is in compliance with all Health Insurance Portability and Accountability Act (HIPAA) laws?

A. Beneficence

B. Fairness

C. Transparency

D. Confidentiality

10. The food bank and the healthcare clinics have developed a document indicating their common interests in serving the health of the people of the community and their willingness to provide referrals to each other's organizations. The document does not specify things more specific than that. That document can best be described as a:

A. Memorandum of Understanding

B. Memorandum of Agreement

C. Memorandum of Collaboration

D. Memorandum of Cooperation

11. The food bank and the community-based Diabetes Prevention Program (DPP) have developed a document specifying that the food bank will refer clients to the community-based DPP program for a certain fee per client. The document also has specific provisions for data sharing and specifies an end date. That document can best be described as a:

A. Memorandum of Understanding

B. Memorandum of Agreement

C. Memorandum of Collaboration

D. Memorandum of Cooperation

12. The food bank is using tablets to collect baseline and follow-up data from clients while they wait in line. Which of the following staff functions could volunteers be used for?

A. Data management

B. Survey development

C. Data entry

D. Data analysis

13. A health educator working in a large city plans to offer nutritional programming at several local federally qualified health clinics aimed at helping those with complex medical needs eat a recommended diet. One barrier to implementing the plan is the lack of staff to lead the classes. What would be a logical next step for the health educator to take?

    A. Abandon the plan as unrealistic
    B. Charge people attending the clinics the cost of the classes, including staff
    C. Reach out to local universities to find student interns from dietitian programs
    D. Use lay volunteers to teach the classes

14. Program plans, timelines, and budgets should be:

    A. Flexible enough to respond to what is learned from pretesting and other feedback
    B. Developed using a software package that provides standard formats and automatic calculations
    C. Developed by the planning team, agreed upon by stakeholders, and rigidly adhered to
    D. A and B

15. Program budgets are most often monitored:

    A. Hourly
    B. Daily
    C. Monthly
    D. Yearly

16. A health educator is asked to sit on a panel conducting reviews of funding proposals for community block grants. Which of the following is the health educator least likely to take under consideration when making his or her recommendation on whether to fund a particular proposal

    A. The volunteer training plan
    B. The research aims

C. The budget justification

D. The letters of support

17. A local health department is receiving calls expressing concern about the opening of a needle exchange facility in a neighborhood that has been beset with high rates of hepatitis C caused by the sharing of needles. The needle exchange facility is needed to reduce the exposure of injection drug users to infectious diseases, but the community's concerns need to be addressed. Which of the following methods would be the most effective and realistic way of gathering concerns from the community and exploring mutually agreeable solutions?

   A. Conduct random digit dialing telephone interviews with community residents.

   B. Go door to door in the neighborhoods to interview people about their concerns.

   C. Mail surveys to homes in the neighborhood.

   D. With community partners, hold community meetings about the proposed facility.

18. A health educator wants to evaluate a partnership between his organization and the Heart Health Organization on a program to identify older people in the community with high blood pressure and help them eat better and become more physically active. A logic model is a frequent starting point for an evaluation because:

   A. It is prepared by participants

   B. It lists activities and outcomes

   C. It is prepared by experts

   D. It is a diagram

19. Which of the following is the least important to include when you are posting a job description?

   A. Job title

   B. Summary of responsibilities

   C. Educational requirements

   D. Number of vacation days

20. An organization has been awarded funds to develop a training kit to help public health nurses persuade vaccine-hesitant parents to catch their children up on recommended childhood vaccines. A progress report is due at the end of the year on the planned grant activities and the grant spending. Which of the following would be the first step in preparing the report for the funder?

    A. Reviewing the stated requirements for the report
    B. Gathering the available data
    C. Drafting the report
    D. Preparing and executive summary

ANSWERS

1. C. Health Insurance Portability and Accountability Act

The Health Insurance Portability and Accountability Act of 1996 (HIPAA) prohibits the sharing of most individually identifiable information, though there are exceptions including those for public health protections such as reportable diseases.

2. C. Create job descriptions for the volunteer positions

The first step would be to determine what tasks could be filled by volunteers and write the job descriptions for the volunteer positions. Until you know what you need people to be doing, you cannot offer trainings or advertise the positions on social media (or anywhere else). Developing a website for tracking hours may or may not be appropriate, given project resources, volunteer preferences, and job requirements.

3. C. Motivating

Budgets are helpful for planning, monitoring, and making decisions about program activities.

4. D. Who is included in an IRB review panel

The taken-for-granted assumptions about health, healthcare, and health systems that we live and work with are part of our dominant health paradigm. How, to you, does the dominant paradigm of health influence you and your work? What assumptions to you bring to the table when you think about your job? How might those be different from those you work with? What challenges do those differences create?

5. C. A and B

While it might be nice to receive feedback from all related social service organizations in the area, it is likely unrealistic to think time and resources will permit it. At a minimum, feedback should, however, be obtained from the organization's management and staff and key stakeholders.

6. C. The candidate's childcare arrangements

Areas of Federal Law and some state laws prohibit discriminating against employees due to their status as parents or caregivers. Interviewers must avoid asking direct questions about whether candidates have children, their ages, and what childcare arrangements are in place.

7. B. To understand how they functioned in their past employment, educational, or volunteer experience

Contacting references can give you, as the potential future employer, a sense of how the candidate functioned in their past work, educational, or volunteer environment. However, those environments may dramatically differ from your organizations, and certainly cannot guarantee that this candidate is the right person for the job. It is also the best practice to independently verify with the candidate's educational or credentialing organization that they do indeed hold the degrees/certifications they claim to—many organizations skip this step, so you cannot take it for granted that their last workplace did so.

8. C. Clinicaltrials.gov

Clinicaltrials.gov is a website that maintains information about clinical trials. The others would be appropriate sources of funding.

9. D. Confidentiality

HIPPA laws are designed to protect the privacy of patients and their healthcare information.

10. A. Memorandum of Understanding

A Memorandum of Understanding (or MOU) is a broad document indicating common interests and intended actions, but it is not specific or legally enforceable.

11. B. Memorandum of Agreement

A Memorandum of Agreement is a document specifying work on a specific project that has been agreed upon and outlining terms and responsibilities of each partner.

12. C. Data entry

Trained volunteers could assist with data entry functions. Survey development, data management (including monitoring, cleaning, and reporting), and analysis are best left to professionals.

13. C. Reach out to local universities to find student interns from dietician programs

Using student interns would be a way to provide staff to lead classes who have technical knowledge but who would likely not add substantial costs to a program.

14. A. Flexible enough to respond to what is learned from pretesting and other feedback

Planning requires flexibility to respond to unexpected changes. Always budget—in both time and money—for things to come up. Software packages and sample budgets from other projects can be helpful for planning, but each project requires its own budget. It would be unusual to have a wide group of stakeholders comment on project budget and timeline, and projects usually require some flexibility when it comes to plans, budgets, and timelines.

15. C. Monthly

Those responsible for monitoring program budgets typically do so monthly, unless there is some reason to do so more frequently (i.e., cash flow is very tight).

16. A. The volunteer training plan

Research aims, budget justification, and letters of support are critical to most if not all funding proposals.

17. D. With community partners, hold community meetings about the proposed facility

Holding face-to-face community meetings in conjunction with community partners would be the most financially and time-efficient method of hearing community concerns while being able to explore potential solutions.

18. B. It lists activities and outcomes

A logic model lists inputs, activities, outputs, and outcomes expected of a program. With this information, an evaluation can be planned.

19. D. Number of vacation days

Typically, the number of vacation days is a negotiated benefit.

20. A. Reviewing the stated requirements for the report

The first step is to review what the funder has required for the report. Many funders have specific requirements for their reports in content and/or structure. Before beginning a report, you must know what it is you are supposed to be reporting.

REFERENCES

Caburnay, C. A., Kreuter, M. W., & Donlin, M. J. (2001). Disseminating effective health promotion programs from prevention research to community organizations. *Journal of Public Health Management and Practice, 7*, 81–89. doi:10.1097/00124784-200107020-00011

Centers for Disease Control and Prevention. (n.d.). Strategic planning. Retrieved from https://www.cdc.gov/healthyYouth/evaluation/pdf/spcards_v3.pdf

Centers for Disease Control and Prevention, & Oak Ridge Institute for Science and Education. (2002). *CDCynergy web: Your guide to successful health communication.* Retrieved from https://www.orau.gov/cdcynergy/web/default.htm

Emmons, K. M., & Rollnick, S. (2001). Motivational interviewing in health care settings: Opportunities and limitations. *American journal of preventive medicine, 20*(1), 68–74. doi:10.1016/s0749-3797(00)00254-3

Graham, J. D., Corso, P. S., Morris, J. M., Segui-Gomez, M., & Weinstein, M. C. (1998). Evaluating the cost-effectiveness of clinical and public health measures. *Annual review of public health, 19*(1), 125–152. doi:10.1146/annurev.publhealth.19.1.125

Israel, B. A., Schulz, A. J., Parker, E. A., & Becker, A. B. (1998). Review of community-based research: Assessing partnership approaches to improve public health. *Annual review of public health, 19*(1), 173–202. doi:10.1146/annurev.publhealth.19.1.173

Macdowall, W., Bonnell, C., & Davies, M. (2006). *Health promotion practice.* Maidenhead, Berkshire, UK: McGraw-Hill.

Merzel, C., & D'Afflitti, J. (2003). Reconsidering community-based health promotion: Promise, performance, and potential. *American journal of public health, 93*(4), 557–574. doi:10.2105/ajph.93.4.557

Novick, L. F., & Mays, G. P. (2005). *Public health administration: Principles for population-based management.* Burlington, MA: Jones & Bartlett.

Royeen, C. B., Jensen, G. M., & Harvan, R. A. (2011). *Leadership in interprofessional health education and practice.* Burlington, MA: Jones & Bartlett.

Wright, K., Hann, N., McLeroy, K. R., Steckler, A., Matulionis, R. M., Auld, M. E., … Weber, D. L. (2003). Health education leadership development: A conceptual model and competency framework. *Health Promotion Practice, 4*(3), 293–302. doi:10.1177/1524839903004003014

Wright, K., Rowitz, L., Merkle, A., Reid, W. M., Robinson, G., Herzog, B., Weber, … Baker, E. (2000). Competency development in public health leadership. *American Journal of Public Health, 90*(8):1202–1207. doi:10.2105/AJPH.90.8.1202

Chapter 7

Area VI: Serve As a Health Education/Promotion Resource Person

INTRODUCTION

To those who have not yet accumulated much work experience as a health educator, this may seem the competency with which you are the least familiar. On the other hand, to those who have been working in the field a while, there is likely much in this section that may seem familiar. A health educator is often called upon to be a resource person—a source of information about public-health related topics—as part of their job duties. For example, schools might need a health educator to make sure that a health curriculum they are considering implementing is evidence based and meets local, state, and national standards and/or be called upon to assess its suitability and acceptability for students, faculty, staff, and families. Alternatively, a local community-based organization (CBO) might need to find information on a certain disease or condition that is affecting the population, as well as search for potential treatments, preventive information, or funding to combat the problem. As a final example, a hospital might be interested in reducing emergency room use for nonemergent conditions, and wish to consult with a health educator to understand what other hospitals have done to reduce inappropriate use and then create communication materials describing more appropriate avenues of care. In whatever setting, health educators are often called upon to identify appropriate, credible, and ethical information and then convey that information to a variety of audiences using a variety of methods. In this chapter, we review the best ways to obtain and disseminate health information to multiple audiences.

A second function of health education frequently mentioned in job descriptions is the ability to perform trainings. Health educators are well placed to provide training because we are able to identify and synthesize health-related information and then communicate it in a training session using a variety of educational techniques. The skills and information discussed in this section will be distinct from those discussed in Chapter 4 on training staff to implement health education/promotion programs.

Finally, we review the third major competency under this area, "Serve as a health education consultant." Sometimes health educators are asked to consult by an outside organization—public or private. This kind of consultation can cover a wide range of topics, settings, and levels of involvement. A health educator might be asked to facilitate a meeting, evaluate a program, and deliver information on a specific topic such as diabetes or flu shots. Many organizations find it preferable to hire consultants when needed rather than maintain a full-time health educator.

If these topics are new to you, do not worry—for many health educators, this is among the most challenging and rewarding parts of the job!

OBTAIN AND DISSEMINATE HEALTH INFORMATION[1]

Health educators are often called upon to . . . well, educate people about health. The health education part of the job is distinct from program planning, implementation, evaluation, and so on. It is closely linked to health communication, which is covered in Chapter 8. At its heart, this function is essentially obtaining and disseminating health information. The basic steps to doing this kind of education are the following:

1. Assessing the need for education
2. Identifying valid information sources
3. Crafting messages
4. Disseminating information
5. Assessing understanding and providing additional information

In the following sections we will go over each step in depth and share our experiences conducting health information to adult learners.

A word about health education: The information discussed here will be largely in the context of adult education. There are National Health

---

[1] NCHEC Competency 6.1. Obtain and disseminate health-related information.

Education Standards (NHES) that are written expectations for what students should know and be able to do by Grades 2, 5, 8, and 12 to promote personal, family, and community health; however, in most school districts, primary and secondary teachers are required to have additional training and credentialing to work in public schools. This guide will discuss school-based settings only at the administrative level, rather than the direct educational level. Although many public school teachers do hold Certified Health Education Specialist (CHES®) certification, it is not the only credential necessary for those jobs, and competencies were not written to fully support the work of K–12 public school teachers.

ASSESS NEEDS FOR INFORMATION

By now, it will come as no surprise that we begin the process of providing education by assessing needs. Sometimes these needs will be obvious (e.g., you are asked by your boss to provide a training in health literacy to nurses who work in your unit), and sometimes it will be your job to assess what the needs are in your particular work setting (e.g., you are in charge of workforce development or a training director). Remember, from Chapter 2, the steps of a needs assessment:

1. Determine the purpose of the needs assessment.
2. Identify available data to assess the problem.
3. Decide on data collection approach and gather data.
4. Analyze and interpret the data.
5. Identify factors linked to the problem (in this case, the lack of sufficient knowledge).
6. Identify the focus of the training and begin the planning process.

In this, as in all needs assessments, you must always be mindful of what your available resources are. Resources are largely composed of time, money, and staff. While the earlier steps seem formal, they can be done with varying levels of resources.

The next two considerations to remember when developing a training needs assessment: First, remember to include stakeholders who can provide you valuable insights to what the needs of the audiences are. Stakeholders can also sometimes augment resources if you have identified a gap in what is available and what is needed. Maybe they can provide food, materials, or a place if you are planning on doing your education face-to-face, such as a half-day training meeting. Alternatively, maybe they can host a web page on their website or have a printing budget you could use to print brochures or booklets. The second is to make sure your needs assessment is theory-based. In Chapter 2, we covered some of the typical theories and models used in needs assessment. Again, the use of theories and models can be formal and complex or more rapid and scaled-down, but regardless of which your resources and needs support, a systematic, logical approach should always be used!

Next, you have to gather your data to support your assessment of your training needs. As discussed in Chapter 2, there are a lot of ways to gather this data, both qualitatively and quantitatively. Your worksite, for example, might have a health risk assessment (HRA) that gives you some insight that perhaps your employees need some education about what are low-risk levels of alcohol use. Or, reviewing your home visiting nurses' notes might reveal that they are spending a lot of time helping their clients prepare healthy meals but are frustrated by a lack of recipes that are inexpensive and easy to make. Those are both examples of using primary data—data you have collected and analyzed. You might instead be looking at secondary data—data that someone else have collected and analyzed. An example of using secondary data might be if you were working as a health educator in the county health department and you reviewed Centers for Disease Control and Prevention's (CDC's) Behavioral Risk Factor Surveillance System (BRFSS) and discovered that your community has particularly high levels of skin cancer.

Not all health needs, clearly, can be fully addressed through the delivery of information. In this section, however, we are focusing on issues that can—at least partly—be addressed by education. Depending on what your needs assessment finds, make note of issues that may not be fully addressed by education alone, and revisit them at a later date to identify what other interventions might be needed.

Hopefully, at this point you are left with an idea of what your audience's needs are for information. You can then move into the next stage, planning your educational or training intervention.

IDENTIFY VALID INFORMATION RESOURCES

When it comes to obtaining health information, to paraphrase Charles Dickens, now truly is the best of times AND the worst of times. Never in human history has there been such unfettered access to such large amounts of information. At any time of the day or night, from anywhere that has access to an Internet connection (at least in countries that allow unfettered Internet access!) you can find just about any kind of information, opinion, data, or question on nearly any topic imaginable (though the Internet still cannot tell me where I left my glasses, unfortunately.) On the good side, health educators in the 21st century have close to the sum of human knowledge at their fingertips: we can look up the correct dosing for a 2-year-old's ibuprofen, the number of calories in a medium-sized apple, or best practices for smoking cessation. On the down side, however, there is also a lot of misleading, outdated, biased, and just plain wrong information out there as well—and not just on the Internet but in books, TV shows, radio, and from your friends and family (sorry, Mom.) The sheer volume of information available itself can be overwhelming—how do we find good sources of accurate information quickly? This is a critical skill for health educators to develop. In fact, in modern times, it seems less important to know some particular fact or piece of information than to know where to get a particular fact or piece of information.

Separating good information from bad and finding what information you need out of all the information available will be necessary for your professional development. While it is impossible to list all of the sources of good information or to guarantee that everything you find even from reliable sources is true, useful, and up to date, there are some basic guidelines to help you narrow your search and think critically about what you find.

Books, pamphlets, journal articles, and professional presentations are just some of the many sources of information you may be asked to review. In general, items that have been peer reviewed (such as articles from juried scientific journals) or are from governmental sources are considered more likely to be accurate and free from bias, but even then we should not rely on only one source of information—many times studies published in peer-reviewed literature have later been disproven or disputed. Major professional associations such as the American Medical Association, American Academy of Pediatrics, American Public Health Association, Society of Public Health Educators, and others are also considered legitimate sources of information, though the same caveats apply. Books are harder to judge, and require knowing whether the author is someone legitimate or not. Credentials can help you determine that, as well as if the book has been reviewed by others you know to be credible (many peer-reviewed journals do book reviews). A librarian can help you judge whether the information in a book fits what you are looking for. As always, if you are seeing similar information from a variety of sources, you can feel more confident it is good information.

HILL'S CRITERIA FOR CAUSATION

It is often observed that "correlation does not equal causation"—but how can causation be established? There are certainly multiple schools of thought on the issue, but Hill (1965) posited a set of nine criteria which provide evidence of causation, at least from the epidemiological perspective. These criteria are the following:

1. Strength: The larger the association, the more likely it is causal.

2. Consistency: Consistent findings observed by different persons in different places with different samples strengthen the likelihood that there is a causal relationship.

3. Specificity: The more specific an association is between a factor and an effect, the larger the chance of a causal relationship.

4. Temporality: The effect has to occur after the cause.

5. Biological gradient: (sometimes called dose response)—Greater exposure should generally lead to greater effect.

6. Plausibility: Does the relationship seem plausible?

7. Coherence: Coherence between epidemiological and laboratory findings increases the likelihood of an effect.

8. Experiment: Presence of experimental evidence.

9. Analogy: The effect of similar factors may be considered, for example, the effects of thalidomide when judging the effects of other drugs on birth defects.

Questions to ask to assess online health information (adapted from National Cancer Institute's [2002] *Making Health Communication Programs Work: A Planner's Guide*)

- From whom is the information? It should be abundantly clear from the page who is responsible for the information. Individual authors may be listed, and if so, should include their credentials. Otherwise information may be authored, but should be clearly marked as to whom the information is from.

- Where does the funding come from? It should be clear who is funding the information. Many websites exist that have generic-sounding names but really are funded by groups with specific interests. A good place to look is the "About Us" section or an online search on what the organization is or who it is funded by.

- Is the organization the original source of information, or is it reposting someone else's information? All original source material should be clearly cited so you can judge whether it is up to date, relevant, and methodologically sound.

- Is there a review process or information clearance process before information is posted? Most legitimate sources of health information have someone with medical, public health, or similar credentials review information to make sure it is correct. A search on the site should reveal what their process is, and who is in charge of reviewing information.

- When was the information last updated or reviewed? The page should have a note indicating when it was last updated or had its information reviewed. Some topics have rapidly evolving information, so consider whether the information you are viewing is likely to have changed recently.

- What is the site's privacy/use policy? This is very important, particularly if you are entering in information about any personal health topics.

A Word About Domain Names

Many savvy heath educators look at domain names (part of the URL, or web address) as a way to assess where information is coming from. As a reminder, in the United States, a government agency has .gov in the address. An educational institution is indicated by .edu in the address. A professional organization such as a scientific or research society will be identified as .org. For example, the American Heart Association's website is www.heart.org. Commercial sites are identified by a .com or .net or .biz or a number of other domains. Research has shown that people tend to trust information from .gov and .edu websites the most, but remember, these are not hard-and-fast rules. Just because something has a .edu or .org domain name does not mean that the information is correct or free from bias. Domain names are simply one tool to help you determine who the information is from.

Following is a list of information resources that are generally considered trustworthy. This list is by no means exhaustive, and it is quite possible that even these reputable sources might make mistakes, but these are a good place to start.

Governmental

The World Health Organization (www.who.int)—The World Health Organization's primary role is "to direct and coordinate international health within the United Nations' system."

U.S. Department of Health and Human Services (DHHS; www.dhhs .gov)—"The mission of the DHHS is to enhance and protect the health and well-being of all Americans. We fulfill that mission by providing for effective health and human services and fostering advances in medicine, public health, and social services."

Under DHHS, there are a number of health- and research-related organizations that are excellent sources of information.

- CDC (www.cdc.gov)
- Agency for Healthcare Research and Quality (www.ahrq.gov)
- Agency for Toxic Substances and Disease Registry (www.atsdr .cdc.gov)
- Centers for Medicare and Medicaid Services (www.cms.gov)
- Food and Drug Administration (www.fda.gov)
- Health Resources and Services Administration (www.hrsa.gov)
- Indian Health Services (www.ihs.gov)
- National Institutes of Health (www.nih.gov)
- Substance Abuse and Mental Health Services Administration (SAMHSA; www.samhsa.gov)

Organizations

CBOs or, a term more commonly used internationally, nongovernmental organizations (NGOs), can be excellent sources of information—or not. All the same caveats listed earlier apply when assessing their information. Examples of highly trusted information include the following:

American Heart Association (www.heart.org)

American Cancer Society (www.cancer.org)

American Red Cross (www.redcross.org)

American Public Health Association (www.apha.org)

Society for Public Health Educators (www.sophe.org)

Foundations can also be a wonderful source of reputable health information. It is important with them, as with other organizations, to understand their motives, funding, and methods. The Foundation Center (www .foundationcenter.org) can help you become familiar with foundations that you might need to investigate. Examples of commonly cited foundations include the following:

The Robert Wood Johnson Foundation (www.rwjf.org)

The Henry J. Kaiser Family Foundation (www.kff.org)

The Pew Internet and American Life Project (www.pewinternet.org)

Finally, policy or research centers or "think tanks" are organizations devoted to advancing policies or research in a particular area or topic. Given that they often have an agenda of some kind, you should be aware of their funding and motivation, but they can be highly valued information sources. Examples of such centers who do work in public health are the following:

Rand Corporation (www.rand.org)

The Pew Research Center (www.pewresearch.org)

RTI International (www.rti.org)

Finally, there are a number of searchable databases for health information. These may contain access to journals, white papers, abstracts, evidence-based programs, and databases. Some of them require subscriptions, which may be available through workplaces, local libraries, or professional organizations. Some examples are the following:

Cumulative Index to Nursing and Allied Health Literature (CINAHL):
The CINAHL database accesses nursing and allied health literature
covering a wide range of topics including nursing, biomedicine,
health sciences librarianship, alternative/complementary medicine,
consumer health, and 17 allied health disciplines. Membership is
required. Available at www.CINAHL.com

EBMR: The Evidence-Based Medicine Reviews is a collection of
databases that contain evidence-based strategies, program,
and clinical information including the Cochrane Database of
Systematic Reviews. Some information is available for free, others
require a fee. Available at www.ovid.com

ERIC: The Education Resource Information Center has journals
related to school health, school-aged children, and education

generally. It is free to use (full-text articles may require payment). Available at https://eric.ed.gov

MEDLINE: One of the go-to-sources for medical and public health data. PubMed provides free access to the database, though accessing the full text of certain articles may not be free. Available at www.ncbi.nlm.nih.gov/pubmed

PsycINFO: As the name suggests, this database contains journal articles, abstracts, books, white papers, and dissertations related to psychology and behavioral science. There is a fee. Available at www.apa.org/pubs/databases/psycinfo

Sources of evidence-based programs:

Many health educators will want to be familiar with sources of evidence-based programs, or programs that have been shown to be reliable and valid (at least for certain populations). Following are the examples of common places to find evidence-based programs:

Community Health Online Resource Center (https://nccd.cdc.gov/ DCH_CHORC)

Effective Interventions: HIV Prevention that Works (https:// effectiveinterventions.cdc.gov)

Healthy People 2020 Evidence-based Resources (www.healthypeople .gov/2020/tools-resources/Evidence-Based-Resources)

SAMHSA's National Registry of Evidence-based Programs and Practices (www.nrepp.samhsa.gov/landing.aspx)

U.S. Preventive Services Task Force (www .uspreventiveservicestaskforce.org)

The Community Guide (www.thecommunityguide.org/ task-force-findings)

CONVEY HEALTH-RELATED INFORMATION TO POPULATIONS AND STAKEHOLDERS

Once you have identified the needed health information, you have to prepare it for dissemination to your audience. Remember, you must carefully consider your audience at this stage—what do you know about them? Parents of third graders in a school with a measles outbreak are going to have very different questions than a group of public health nurses or the county superintendent, and different levels of detail, presentation methods, and tones will be required for each.

DISSEMINATE INFORMATION

Your final task in finding and disseminating health information is actually disseminating the information. Here, as always, a thorough knowledge of your audience is appropriate, whether you are providing the information to the population or key stakeholders. While it is often obvious who the populations you are working with, let us take a minute to review who some of the potential stakeholders you might need to remember

- Program management and staff
- Funders (or those you fund)
- Coalitions/advocacy programs who are interested in your topic (local, regional, state, national)
- Health departments (local, state)
- Schools or educational organizations (local, county, regional, or state)
- Universities or research organizations
- Government (local, county, or state)
- Businesses, chambers of commerce, or other commercial organizations
- Healthcare systems, insurers, clinicians
- Religious or CBOs
- Neighborhood associations or groups
- Law enforcement/justice system
- Population-specific organizations such as a local organization serving the blind or Latinos

If you are not thoroughly familiar with the population or partner and their preferred methods of receiving information, it is helpful to find someone who is and discuss what would be the best methods for disseminating the information. Typically, health educators use a wide variety of dissemination methods including:

- Presentations
- Lectures

- Demonstrations (cooking classes, shopping trips, or baby care classes)
- Printed educational materials (posters, brochures, fact sheets, or infographics)
- Electronic information (webpages, social media posts, videos, interactive graphics, or video games)

Often, more than one technique will be called for, particularly if the information is complex, important, or being presented to various audiences. Utilize your key informants to make sure that your choices, language, visuals, tone, and engagement level are appropriate and acceptable to your audiences, and ask for and be open to feedback.

Conduct Trainings

Another core function of serving as a resource person for health education is providing trainings. For some health educators this represents a substantial portion of their duties, and some will do this only occasionally. Providing trainings[2] has a similar structure to implementing health education classes discussed in Chapter 4, but the audience may be different. Often trainings are provided to other professionals who work with the target population, but need some specific piece of information to share with their audiences. For example, a health educator might be asked to train nurses at a hospital on health literacy, or county human service workers on the needs of postpartum women and infants during a natural disaster. Of course, the line of distinction of what is training to a professional audience and what is education aimed at a population is not clear. Regardless, knowing who your audience is and understanding their wants and needs for the training is critical.

Assessing the needs of your audience is the first step in designing effective trainings. These might be provided to you depending on how the request for the training arrives. For example, you might be told, "Please design a 2-hour training for nurses at a women's hospital on health literacy that includes Teach Back training." How would you go about that? Ideally, you would know how many people you could expect at your training, what their level of knowledge about the topic was, and if they had any specific requests for information to be included. Sometimes this information may be available before hand, sometimes not—it never hurts to ask!

---

[2] NCHEC Competency 6.2. Train others to use health education/promotion skills.

Even if you cannot access this information before hand, you can always do a quick assessment at the beginning of the training and adjust your plans to meet the audience's needs while you are delivering it.

Adult Learning

Learning is a lifelong process.

Many instructors have wondered how best to design meaningful and engaging instruction. Gagne, Briggs, and Wager (1992) identified several mental and behavioral conditions on which learning is predicated. These are based on the way adults process information when they are presented with various stimuli. Gagne et al. identified a nine-step process called the events of instruction, which correlate to and address the conditions of learning.

The Nine Events of Instruction are the following:

1. Gain attention
2. Inform learners of objectives
3. Stimulate recall of prior learning
4. Present the content
5. Provide "learning guidance"
6. Elicit performance (practice)
7. Provide feedback
8. Assess performance
9. Enhance retention and transfer to the job

Once you have assessed the needs as best you can, it is time to design your training. While there are lots of ways to develop a training, let us review some tips for good oral presentations.

Plan your time wisely. Aim to finish each training early. Things often do not run totally smoothly, so allow time for the audience to arrive a little late, for audiovisual hiccups to happen, and for audience questions. Things often take a little longer when you are in an unfamiliar environment, so leave yourself time to adjust.

Plan for breaks. Most adults can only pay attention and really focus for a short period of time. If you are planning a training of more than an hour or so, plan on taking quick breaks or transitioning from one activity to another to keep learners engaged.

Utilize a variety of teaching strategies. If you think back to some of our most effective teachers over the years, what do you remember? Someone who lectured to you without stopping for the entire time? Or someone who used different techniques to keep the class interesting? Here are some examples of types of teaching strategies you can employ beyond lecturing:

- Brainstorming
- Debates
- Gaming
- Group work
- Discussion
- Dramatic role-play
- Hands-on demonstrations
- Guest speakers or team teaching (including video or over the Internet)
- Panel discussion
- Problem solving
- Simulators
- Training on equipment

Likewise, you will probably have greater success in your training if you share information through a variety of methods. Here are some channels to consider:

- DVDs
- Handouts
- Internet
- Pamphlets
- Posters
- Models
- Study guides
- Worksheets
- Workbooks
- Videos

Use presentation software wisely. Presentation software can help trainees learn by reinforcing important content visually, but like any tool it can be used well or badly. While there are no hard-and-fast rules when it comes to using presentation software, consider these guidelines from the www.asha.org/Events/convention/PowerPoint-Do-s-and-Don-ts:

- Use legible type size. Titles should be at least 36 to 40 points, bulleted text at least 24 points.

- Be brief. Aim for key words or phrases to reinforce your message, not paragraphs of text. Make every word and image count!

- Make it readable. Use normal case (not all caps). Remember health literacy principles.

- Limit the number of slides. A good rule of thumb is one slide per minute of your presentation (but not for multiple-hour presentations!)

- Do not overuse special effects. Use sound, animation, and other effects very sparingly, if at all. They often are simply as distraction.

- Do not use more than eight words per line or eight lines per slide.

- Avoid hard-to-read color combinations such as red/green, brown/green, blue/black, blue/purple. Aim for high contrast between background and text.

Check in with your audience frequently. You can gauge how your audience is responding to your training verbally and nonverbally. Do they look attentive, bored, or confused? Consider taking a short "quiz break" every section or topic to see if they are understanding the information. Frequently stop and ask for questions.

Evaluating Your Training

Evaluation is conducted for a number of reasons. According to Kirkpatrick and Kirkpatrick (2016), evaluations of training are conducted for three primary reasons: to improve the program, to maximize transfer of learning to behavior, and to show the value of the training to the organization/stakeholders. All of these are worthy reasons. Kirkpatrick and Kirkpatrick propose there are four levels of evaluation of training and that there are appropriate methods to evaluate each one. Level 1 is to gauge reaction—that is, to understand the participant's feelings about the training by gauging satisfaction and engagement. That can best be accomplished by surveys or feedback forms. Level 2 is to gauge learning, or how much the training changed knowledge, attitudes, or skills. A pretest–posttest can provide the trainer with that information. Level 3 gauges behavior, or the extent to which the trainees apply their new information, skills, and so on on the job. That can be evaluated over time with interviews or observations. Finally, Level 4 gauges results, which is whether the change in behavior seen at Level 3 has any effect on the organization, target population, and so on. The techniques for evaluating results would vary between situations, but might involve reviewing secondary data to see if there were improvements in client outcomes, procedures, and so on. Naturally, not all trainings are evaluated at all the four levels. Level 1 is the most frequently evaluated, followed by Level 2. Levels 3 and 4 are rarely employed because of lack of resources.

CONSULTING[3]

Health educators may either act as or need to hire consultants. In this section, we will discuss issues relative to both situations. Let us address being hired as a consultant first. Occasionally, an organization will hire a consultant if they need to address a problem or situation but do not have an employee with the knowledge or capacity to address the situation. For example, imagine a police department is interested in improving its response to mental and behavioral health issues by increasing referrals to social service and behavioral health and substance abuse treatment., but they do not want to hire someone full time to do that work. Instead, they could hire a consultant to advise them how best to train their officers to identify situations in which mental health and substance abuse issues are relevant and make appropriate referrals. This is referred to as external consulting, when a health educator provides information or guidance to an organization or company he or she does not normally work with. The relationship is considered to be formal if there is a written contract.

On the other hand, as a health educator, you may be in a situation where your organization is in need of hiring a consultant to provide you with temporary support on a project. When selecting a consultant, your organization may follow a process that looks something like the following:

1. Identify if and why a consultant might be necessary for your project.
2. Check to see if all internal resources have been exhausted.
3. Solicit bids.

---

[3] NCHEC Competency 6.3. Provide advice and consultation on health education/promotion issues.

4. Assess the bids based on various criteria including fees, availability, experience, references, and prior work with your organization.

5. Interview the top candidates.

6. Hire your top pick. Retain the names of other qualified consultants for use on future projects or in case the initial choice does not work out or does not accept the job. These names may also be potential hires for jobs in the future—it is not unusual for people to move in and out of regular employment and consultative work, so keep networking or maintaining informal relationships with people and organizations. You never know when it may be useful to your career or your organization!

CONCLUSION

Many health educators spend considerable time serving as a resource person, trainer, or consultant to a variety of clients. As with other kinds of interventions, assessing needs, planning, implementing, and evaluating work help ensure that resources are not wasted and that maximal benefit is achieved. In the next chapter, you will review the final competency, Area VII: Communicate, Promote, and Advocate for Health, Health Education/Promotion and the Profession.

REVIEW QUESTIONS

1. A health educator is developing a training class for teachers to start peer health education programs in their schools. Which of the following would be the correct order of steps to develop the training?

   A. Determine training needs>Select participants>Set objectives>Develop training materials>Determine training content

   B. Set objectives>Determine training needs>Select participants>Develop training materials>Determine training content

   C. Set objectives>Determine training needs>Determine training content>Develop training materials>Select participants

   D. Determine training needs>Set objectives>Determine training content>Develop training materials>Select participants

2. Which of the following is not a characteristic of e-learning?

   A. e-Learning is rarely used to complement other kinds of training
   B. e-Learning is not as effective as traditional training methods
   C. e-Learning cannot be usefully blended with other training methods
   D. e-Learning has not been widely adopted for training in workplaces

3. A health educator is asked to find elementary school health resources for substance abuse prevention. The most appropriate database to search would be:

   A. ERIC
   B. CINAHL
   C. EBMR
   D. PsycINFO

4. A health educator buys an "off the shelf" evidence-based curriculum that has been designed for older teens but wants to adapt it for use in younger teens. Which of the following changes that he or she might make would be the most problematic when adapting this program to a younger audience?

   A. Switching fonts in the materials to something more "fun"
   B. Using pictures of younger children
   C. Rewriting instructions to include simpler language
   D. Switching theories of behavior change

5. When adapting evidence-based programs to different audiences, it is a good idea for the health educator to do which of the following:

   A. Implement many small changes rather than a few big changes
   B. Reach out to the program's originators to discuss adaptations
   C. Only substitute pictures of the original target audience for those of the new target audience
   D. Change the length of the program to fit the audience's attention span

6. A health educator needs to write a literature review about infant mental health in children of mothers with severe and persistent mental illness. Which of the following would be the best database for her to use?

   A. EBMR
   B. PsycINFO
   C. ERIC
   D. MEDLINE

7. Health educators can look for information in a variety of sources. *The New England Journal of Medicine* would be considered a
   _____ source, whereas the *New York Times* would be a
   _____ source.

   A. Primary, secondary
   B. Secondary, tertiary
   C. Reliable, unreliable
   D. Valid, reliable

8. According to Bloom's Taxonomy, which classification of skills include the ability to appraise, argue, defend, critique, select, value, or weigh?

   A. Remember
   B. Apply
   C. Evaluate
   D. Create

9. A health educator is asked to identify some health statistics for program planning purposes. All of the following would be reliable sources to get health statistics except:

   A. The U.S. census
   B. The National Center for Health Statistics
   C. State health department websites
   D. TV newscasts

10. Which of the following is the most commonly used social media site by Americans?

    A. Twitter
    B. LinkedIn
    C. Facebook
    D. Instagram

11. When considering whether an information source is appropriate, which of the following is the least important for a health educator to consider?

    A. How engaging the material is to the reader
    B. How accurate the material is
    C. The source of the material
    D. How current the material is

12. Which of the following channels may present the most challenging exercise in evaluating the reliability of information presented?

    A. Peer-reviewed journal
    B. TV newscast
    C. Government website
    D. Blog

13. A health educator has been asked to develop information for a local group of breast cancer survivors on returning to work after treatment. Which is the most appropriate source of information to use?

    A. American Heart Association
    B. Bureau of Labor Statistics
    C. American Cancer Society
    D. Health and Healing for a New You

14. A health educator has been tasked with developing a breastfeeding support program. The health educator is looking for evidence-based interventions as part of the planning process. The least helpful resource would be the following:

    A. Education Resource Information Center (ERIC)
    B. Cochrane reviews
    C. The Guide to Community Preventive Services
    D. The Guide to Clinical Preventive Services

15. Which of the following strategies would be best to employ if you were under a tight time line to complete an assignment to gather information on a particular topic with which you were not familiar and needed to make sure you were only getting information from reputable web-based sources?

    A. Determine the political affiliation of the website authors
    B. Review the sources cited on the pages
    C. Only visit pages from domains that end in .gov, .edu, or .org
    D. Only visit pages with advertisements for nonobjectionable products

16. Print materials were selected as the appropriate way to provide take-home messages to reinforce concepts learned at a training about handwashing at work for healthcare workers. The first step for the health educator in developing those training materials would be to:

    A. Set goals and objectives
    B. Write material content
    C. Find engaging graphics
    D. Contact HR to find out who will be attending the training

17. Which of the following is NOT a reason to evaluate trainings?

    A. To justify the reason for having the training and its contribution to the organization
    B. To determine whether to continue the training program
    C. To identify employees who did not pay attention during trainings
    D. To collect information on how to improve the training

SCENARIO for QUESTIONS 18 to 20: A health educator has collected some resources on opioid drug use that has led to significant hospitalizations and deaths in the local county. This information consists of statistics and stories of patients and families of those who died as a result of overdose. The following questions ask about the appropriateness of different ways to communicate the information to various audience members.

18. What would be the best way to present the up-to-date numbers, locations, and types of drugs found to be used in overdoses and deaths when communicating to the public?

    A. An infographic
    B. A pamphlet
    C. A formal report
    D. A literature review

19. What would be the best way to present the up-to-date numbers, locations, and types of drugs found to be used in overdoses and deaths when communicating to the Office of the Mayor?

    A. An infographic
    B. A pamphlet
    C. A formal report
    D. A literature review

20. In this scenario, where the community was struggling with opioid addiction, which would be the least appropriate source to search for evidence-based approaches to address the issue?

    A. Cochrane Reviews
    B. NCI's Research-Tested Intervention Program
    C. SAMHSA's guide to evidence-based practice (EBP)
    D. National Registry of Evidence-based Programs and Practices (NREPP)

ANSWERS

1. D. Determine training needs>Set objectives>Determine training content>Develop training materials>Select participants

The first step is to determine training needs of the audience. Second, you would set objectives for the training, out of which then your content and materials would be developed. Once the training was developed, you would select teachers to participate in your trainings.

2. B. e-Learning is not as effective as traditional training methods

E-learning has become widely adopted across a variety of industries. e-Learning can be blended with traditional methods, can involve using technology to deliver traditional lecture-style training (such as a webinar), deliver non–instructor-based learning, offer social-learning opportunities, and is increasingly being developed for mobile applications.

3. A. ERIC

The Education Resource Information Center (ERIC) contains journals related specifically to school health, children who are school aged, and educational settings and techniques. It is available at www.eric.ed.gov.

4. D. Switching theories of behavior change

There is always some concern when adapting evidence-based curriculum to different audiences because they have been proven to work in a certain audience/space/time and are not guaranteed to do so elsewhere. However, generally, minor changes that make an intervention more tailored to a different, but somewhat similar audience should not change the core of the program greatly. Changes to the heuristics of messages—such as fonts and pictures—and tailoring instructions, (or other programmatic components such as incentives or activities)—as long as it is tested and monitored—should not present a seismic shift in the program. Changing the theoretical foundation of a program, however, changes the whole nature of the program.

5. B. Reach out to the program's originators to discuss adaptations

If possible, it is a good idea when adaption programs to reach out to the developer of the original program to discuss any changes to the program you are considering making. In some cases, this is required when using the program. The program developers may have insight into adaptions that have been tried and how successful (or not) they were.

6. B. PsycINFO

PsychINFO is an online database with more than three million records dedicated to the peer-reviewed literature in the behavioral sciences and mental health.

7. A. Primary, secondary

Original research is considered a primary source. Reporting or coverage of that research—where it may have been translated or interpreted in ways that may have made it easier to understand or relate to—makes it a secondary source.

8. C. Evaluate

Evaluate, or justify, a stand or decision, is the second highest level in Bloom's Taxonomy.

9. D. TV newscasts

TV newscasts would be considered secondary data sources and are not appropriate for gathering data for the purpose of program planning.

10. C. Facebook

According to the Pew Internet and American Life Survey 68% of adults use Facebook. About 25% of adults use the other services.

11. A. How engaging the material is to the reader

While as professionals we would like the material we read to be interesting and engaging, it is not truly required for it to be relevant and valid for our work. What is required is that information be accurate, current, and from a reputable, valid source.

12. D. Blog

Blogs, or weblogs, can be very challenging to assess the validity of information presented on them because they often do not present very clearly the source of the information. They can be written by industry or organizational leaders, or by those with little knowledge or biased opinions. They merit special attention and investigation before citing as a resource.

13. C. American Cancer Society

The American Cancer Society is a national nonprofit voluntary organization that works to fight cancer and support those living with it.

14. A. ERIC

ERIC is a database of education literature and resource. The others are reviews of evidence-based programs.

15. C. Only visit pages from domains that end in .gov, .edu, or .org

While not a perfect strategy, when time is tight or you are unfamiliar with a topic, beginning a search with .gov or .edu resources and possibly adding .org resources (preferably starting with major organizations that are known to be reputable, since anyone can get a .org domain name) is a good first step.

16. D. Contact HR to find out who will be attending the training

Before any decisions can be made about developing materials, first it will be necessary to know who will be attending the training. Will they be doctors? Cafeteria workers? A mix? Have they been to many trainings? Is this their first? What do they know, think, believe? Where in the hospital do they work? How long have they worked here? With this information, you can begin to set goals and objectives and create materials.

17. C. To identify employees who did not pay attention during trainings

Evaluation is focused on understanding how trainings help organizations and how to improve them. They are NOT focused, nor should they be, on penalizing employees.

18. A. An infographic

An infographic can easily show locations, numbers, and dynamically describe statistics in a way that can be more accessible to a lay audience than traditional charts and graphs. It can also be frequently updated and distributed through websites, social media, and traditional print media such as newspapers and flyers.

19. C. A formal report

In contrast to the general public, the Mayor's office is likely to want considerably more information, and is likely to want it in a more formal manner. In this case, you will likely need to prepare a formal report, either in writing or in person, to the Mayor's office.

20. B. NCI's Research-Tested Intervention Program

The National Cancer Institute's (NCI's) Research-Tested Intervention Program is focused on evidence-based programs for cancer. Cochrane

Reviews synthesize research evidence to inform healthcare decision making, including in the prescribing and treating of opioids. SAMHSA, as the nation's substance abuse treatment organization, maintains the guide to EBP and the national registry.

REFERENCES

Gagne, R., Briggs, L., & Wager, W. (1992). *Principles of instructional design* (4th ed.). Fort Worth, TX: HBJ College Publishers.

Hill, Austin Bradford. (1965). The environment and disease: Association or causation?. *Proceedings of the Royal Society of Medicine*, 58(5), 295–300. Retrieved from https://www.ncbi.nlm.nih.gov/pmc/articles/PMC1898525/pdf/procrsmed00196-0010.pdf

Kirkpatrick, J. D., & Kirkpatrick, W. K. (2016). *Four levels of training evaluation*. Alexandria, VA: ATD Press.

National Cancer Institute. (2002). *Making health communication programs work: A planner's guide*. Bethesda, MD: U.S. Department of Health and Human Services, Public Health Service, National Institutes of Health. Retrieved from https://www.cancer.gov/publications/health-communication/pink-book.pdf.

Chapter 8

Area VII: Communicate, Promote, and Advocate for Health, Health Education/Promotion, and the Profession

INTRODUCTION

This chapter covers two different, but related, topics related to health education: advocacy and health communication. In some ways, it is the "everything else" chapter of information that has not been covered up to this point. (As a matter of fact, one of the competencies in this Area is "promote the health education profession," but we already covered the history of the Certified Health Education Specialist (CHES®) credential in Chapter 1, and we will address the information about professional development and opportunities for career advancement in Chapter 10, where we think it is actually a better fit.)[1] Nonetheless, these are skills that are crucial and, particularly in the case of advocacy, which has grown in importance as funding for public health continues to be tight and controversy continues around certain health topics. The past decade has perhaps seen the most change in advocacy, given the wide adoption of the social web and emerging best practices.

---

[1] NCHEC Competency 7.1. Identify, develop, and deliver messages using a variety of communication strategies, methods, and techniques; NCHEC Competency 7.4. Promote the health education profession is covered in Chapter 10.

A health education specialist who practices in a community setting for a disease-specific organization—say, heart disease—will have to be able to develop program materials across a wide range of channels (e.g., pamphlets, websites, social media, and face-to-face at community health fairs). He or she may also have to write letters to the editor, issue press releases, and be available as a resource to the media when stories about heart disease or the organization arise. Additionally, he or she may be asked to provide resources to patients, clinicians, or other organizations to help lobby for funding, resolutions, or legislation, or actually do such lobbying on behalf of his or her organization.

A health education specialist in a collegiate setting might be tasked with developing a tobacco-free campus. He or she would have to educate faculty, staff, and students about the need for such a change and the dangers of smoking and secondhand smoke. He or she would then need to engage with smokers to answer their questions and make sure they understood the upcoming changes and how to access available smoking cessation programs. Appropriate signage, educational materials, and intranet/Internet messaging would need to be developed. The health education specialist would likely work with the media to promote the college's decision throughout the community, and might try to advocate for local laws to be changed to reduce smoking or for additional funding for smoking cessation and prevention programs.

In other settings—school (K–12), healthcare, workplace, and so on—the roles and responsibilities around advocacy and communication are similar. Advocacy and health communication are the two areas where all your skills as a health educator come together to move programs, funding, and education forward within your chosen setting.

INTRODUCTION TO ADVOCACY

Advocacy, or working to bring an issue to a decision-making level—be it within a workplace, school, or local, state, or federal government level—and bring about a desired change, is an increasingly important role for health education specialists. While in the past health educators might have confined themselves largely to education and communication, they are increasingly being called upon to either serve as a resource for advocacy or to engage in advocacy themselves. This section reviews two basic types of advocacy: legislative advocacy and media advocacy. Of course, the distinction between the two is not always clear—the media is often used in trying to change laws, get funding, and so on. But the division provides a helpful way to think about two different audiences (legislators and the media) and how best to interact with each. Like all communication, successful advocacy absolutely depends on a thorough understanding of your audience—what they already know, believe, and want.

Whether a health educator is lobbying to have a law or policy changed or is in the business of helping to craft policies or legislation, the steps to creating comprehensive advocacy campaigns are:

1. Identify current and emerging issues that may influence health and health education.

2. Access accurate resources related to identified issues.

3. Analyze the impact of existing and proposed policies on health.

4. Analyze factors that influence decision makers and identify the significance and implication of health policy for individuals, groups, and communities.

5. Engage stakeholders in advocacy planning and activities.

6. Develop an advocacy plan in compliance with local, state, and/or federal laws and organizational policies and procedures.

7. Communicate the impact of health and health information on organizational and socio-ecological factors, using data where appropriate.

8. Implement advocacy plans for health-related policies, regulations, laws, or rules; use evidence-based research to develop policies to promote health, incorporating media and technology where appropriate.

9. Evaluate advocacy efforts and use evaluation and research findings in policy analysis.

LEGISLATIVE ADVOCACY

Legislative advocacy is, in a nutshell, contacting and working with a policy maker to discuss a public health problem and advocate for some specific solution. These could be as sweeping as raising the drinking age or banning certain types of guns, or such minutia as adjusting reimbursement rates for a particular type of surgical procedure. It can also include **electioneering,** or campaigning for a certain candidate for office. Depending on where you work, direct campaigning or canvassing work may be prohibited during your work time or as part of your work activities; in other jobs, it may be part of your responsibilities. It is always advisable to check with your human resources department to clarify your rights and responsibilities as an employee with regard to advocacy.

It is critical when conducting legislative advocacy to thoroughly understand your audience. You will likely be interacting with one of two types of people: the legislator (government official) themselves, or his or her staff members. Often you begin interacting with a staff member, and then might move on to interacting with the legislator directly. The American Public Health Association (2017) offers these 10 tips for legislative advocacy:

1. Get to know legislators well—their districts and constituencies, voting records, personal schedules, opinions, expertise, and interests. Be sure to have a good understanding of the legislator and his or her concerns, priorities, and perspectives.

2. Acquaint yourself with the staff members for the legislators, committees, and resource officials with whom you will be working. These people are essential sources of information and have significant influence in some instances in the development of policy.

3. Identify fellow advocates and partners in the public health community to better understand the process, monitor legislation, and assess strengths and weaknesses. Finding common ground on an issue sometimes brings together strange bedfellows but makes for a stronger coalition.

4. Identify groups and other legislators with whom you may need to negotiate for changes in legislation. Do not dismiss anyone because of previous disagreements or because you lack a history of working together. "Yesterday's opponent may be today's ally."

5. Foster and strengthen relationships with allies and work with legislators who are flexible and tend to keep an open mind. Do not allow anyone to consider you a bitter enemy because you disagree.

6. Be honest, straightforward, and realistic when working with legislators and their staffs. Do not make promises you cannot keep.

Never lie or mislead a legislator about the importance of an issue, the opposition's position or strength, or other matters.

7. Be polite, remember names, and thank those who help you—both in the legislature and in the public health advocacy community.

8. Learn the legislative process and understand it well. Keep on top of the issues and be aware of controversial and contentious areas.

9. Be brief, clear, accurate, persuasive, timely, persistent, grateful, and polite when presenting your position and communicating what you need/want from the legislator or staff member.

10. Be sure to follow up with legislators and their staff. If you offer your assistance or promise to provide additional information, do so in a timely and professional manner. Be a reliable resource for them today and in the future.

Resources for legislative advocacy:

American Public Health Association (www.apha.org/policies-and-advocacy/advocacy-for-public-health)

Society for Public Health Educators (www.sophe.org/advocacy.cfm)

National Association of County and City Health Officials (www.naccho.org/advocacy)

MEDIA ADVOCACY

Media advocacy attempts to harness the power of the media to change or craft public perception or education around a particular topic. Media can be thought of as "free" or "paid"—free media are stories that are covered by the media, and paid media are advertisements that must be purchased. There are benefits to both. With free media, obviously there is no direct cost to the organization, but you give up control of what is covered. With paid media, you control what is seen, but it can be expensive and the public may perceive it as being more biased than what is covered in the free media. Which kind of media you choose, or what mix, will depend on your budget, interests, and intent. Being skilled in media advocacy means you know who to contact in the media, how to contact them, and how to successfully deliver your message.

Media advocacy often begins with issuing press releases, writing letters to the editor, and/or holding press conferences. For an excellent resource on how to craft these and more, read Centers for Disease Control and Prevention's (CDC) Healthy Community Programs Media Access Guide: A Resource for Community Health Promotion (available at: www.cdc.gov/nccdphp/dch/programs/healthycommunitiesprogram/tools/pdf/mediaaccessguide.pdf).

ADVOCACY EVALUATION

As with any other intervention, evaluation is critical, but is often overlooked in relationship to advocacy. To be able to assess the results of advocacy work, a health education specialist must have gone into the advocacy work with clear goals and SMART (specific, measurable, achievable, relevant, and time-bound) objectives in mind. Thoughtful development of such goals and objectives will pave the way for an effective evaluation. Common evaluation questions related to policy and advocacy include the following:

Process

- Number of communications issued (press releases, blog posts, letters to the editor, etc.)
- Number of meetings held with the community
- Web/social media traffic on the issue
- Number of meetings held with elected officials
- Number of letters/calls to elected officials in support of the organization's position

Impact/Outcome

- Was public awareness of the problem raised?
- Was public support for the desired change increased?
- Were additional people/organizations recruited to the organization/coalition?
- Did the organization gain funding?
- Did support from policy makers increase?
- Was there movement through the legislative process?
- Were policies implemented (or, conversely, blocked or removed)?

HEALTH COMMUNICATION[2]

Health Literacy

Perhaps the most critical element to consider when preparing your information for dissemination is the health literacy level of your audience. Health literacy is the degree to which individuals have the capacity to obtain, process, and understand basic health information and services needed to make appropriate health decisions (U.S. Department of Health and Human Services, 2010).

Health literacy affects a person's ability to:

- Navigate the healthcare system, including filling out complex forms and locating providers and services.
- Share personal information, such as health history, with providers.
- Engage in self-care and chronic disease management.
- Understand mathematical concepts such as probability and risk.

Why Is Health Literacy Important?

While it may seem shocking, according to the National Assessment of Adult Literacy only 12% of U.S. adults have "proficient" levels of health literacy. Fourteen percent of adults (30 million people) have below basic health literacy, and an additional 22% have "basic" levels of health literacy—a combined 36% of the adult population in the United States with insufficient levels of health literacy to be able to fully manage their health. These adults were more likely to report their health as poor (42%) and are more likely to lack health insurance (28%) than adults with proficient health literacy. Indeed, poor health literacy is a better predictor of low health status than age, race, education level, or income (National Center for Education Statistics. 2006).

Who Is at Risk?

Populations most likely to experience low health literacy are

- Older adults
- Racial and ethnic minorities

---

[2] NCHEC Competency 7.2. Engage in advocacy for health and health education/promotion; NCHEC Competency 7.3. Influence policy and/or systems change to promote health and health education.

- People with less than a high school degree (or General Educational Development [GED] certificate)
- People with low income levels
- Nonnative speakers of English
- People with compromised health status

What Comprises Health Literacy?

- Functional literacy
- Numeracy
- Ability to navigate the healthcare system
- Cultural competency

What Is Numeracy?

Health literacy includes numeracy skills, which you can think of as being literacy for numbers and basic math. Just like literacy, people can have high, medium, or low levels.

Low numeracy can affect health because it can make it hard to:

- Understand and manage cholesterol and blood sugar levels.
- Correctly dose medication—for example, knowing the difference between "1 T" and "1 t" of liquid medicine, or finding the appropriate dose based on weight.
- Read nutrition labels, which require people to understand different measurements (e.g., mg, kcals, mcgs) as well as percentages, addition, and so on.
- Buy and use health insurance, which requires the ability to compare different plan prices, co-pays, deductibles, and so on.
- Understand a story in the newspaper about health if it involves reading bar charts, pie charts, and so on.

Here are some tps for producing readable materials:

- Write using plain language. Plain language—or "living room language"—is communication that users can understand the first time they read or hear it.

- Organize your information so that the most important points come first. People with low literacy levels take a longer time to read and may give up partway through a piece. By putting the most important information first, there is a better chance it will be read.

- Break complex information into understandable chunks. Chunking is a valuable tool for helping people understand and retain information. It is why we write phone numbers this way—(888) 555-1212—instead of this way—8885551212. Which would you rather see?

- Use simple language and define technical terms. What are the most important things to do or know?

- Assume people may have trouble with numbers. Many people, even those with higher levels of education, struggle with math and quantitative concepts—particularly statistics. Use only those that are really necessary, and consider using visuals as well as words to convey the information. Sports and gambling analogies are "everyday" language and concepts that may help people understand what you are saying if you have to talk about odds or very small or very large numbers. For example, framing a risk of 1 in 75,000 in terms of "one person at a sold-out game at the Superdome gets sick" might help the audience understand that likelihood, especially if accompanied by a visual of a sold-out game at the Superdome.

- Use the active voice.

- Use commonly available readability programs to check your work. Each population is different, but for a general audience, aim for sixth- to eighth-grade reading level.

- Test your materials with the members of your audience. Words or concepts that sound easy to you may not be so to a less literate population.

Teach-Back Method

One commonly used tool to assess how well information has been understood by an audience is the "teach-back method" (AHRQ, 2015). This method is usually used in face-to-face educational settings. The teacher will teach the information to the student and then ask the student to teach the information back to the teacher. Teach-back is a powerful tool because it simulates a time when learners are on their own trying to use the information or skills they have been given, or are even teaching someone else about what they have been taught. If you are teaching complex information or skills that need multiple steps, you can "chunk and check" at points along the way—that is, do teach-back at different points during the lesson to make sure the student has mastered all the necessary information.

The conversation might go something like this:

Teacher: Now that I have explained to you how to cook chicken, please show me how you are going to test it at home to make sure it is done.

Student: I am going to take the meat thermometer and put it all the way into the chicken breast, but make sure I do not hit the bone.

Teacher: And how will you know it is done?

Student: When it is 165 degrees.

Teacher: So, is this one done?

Student (reading thermometer): 167, so, yes, it is done.

Teacher: That is right—you are ready to go!

Sometimes in using teach-back you discover that there are misunderstandings or pieces of information your students did not learn. Teach-back is a great way to uncover those misunderstandings and be able to correct them. Reimagine the previous scenario, but this time it does not go so smoothly:

Teacher: Now that I have explained to you how to cook chicken, please show me how you are going to test it at home to make sure it is done.

Student: I am going to take the meat thermometer and put it all the way into the chicken breast.

Teacher: Now, we talked about where in the meat to measure the temperature—is that thermometer in the right place?

Student: Oops, no, it is touching the bone. [Backs it out a little]

Teacher: And how will you know it is done?

Student: When it is 145 degrees.

Teacher: I know that is what a lot of people think is safe for chicken breasts, but the U.S. Department of Agriculture (USDA) recommends 165 degrees for chicken breasts, too.

Student: This one is only 150 degrees.

Teacher: So, what are you going to do?

Student: Put it back in the oven for a few minutes and recheck it.

(Few minutes later)

Student: Is this the right place to check the temperature?

Teacher: Looks great! What does the thermometer say?

Student (reading thermometer): 167, so, yes, it is done.

Teacher: That is right—you are ready to go!

CHANNEL SELECTION

Channel selection is a crucial decision in communication planning. Selecting the right channels to relay your message starts identifying the times, places, and states of mind in which your audience is receptive to and able to act upon the information or messages you wish to relay to them. You want to select channels that will reach your intended audiences and deliver the messages to them in a way they understand, want, retain, and can act upon. Think about the lessons discussed in the health literacy section: If people have low levels of literacy, for example, then print channels are best avoided. Audiences who are functionally literate but have low levels of science literacy or numeracy may do best with channels that allow for substantial visual supports, such as video, or interpersonal channels that allow for the assessment of learning such as teach-back. Obviously, cost is another factor that health educators have to consider. Perhaps television advertising would be your first choice because it would reach a lot of people and you could target your audience through placing advertisements on particular shows and times, but the costs of producing and placing those ads are out of the range of your budget. Picking the right mix of channels to go with your messages, audiences, staff time, abilities, and budgets is always a challenge for even the most experienced health educators. Rarely is one channel sufficient to successfully address health education needs. A health educator working at a student health center on stress reduction around finals time might post posters, use digital media boards, hold stress-reduction classes, bring in therapy dogs, and utilize social media all to get stress reduction messages to students. A community health educator trying to get parents in a community with high asthma rates to make and keep follow-up appointments with their child's specialist care providers may produce pamphlets, make reminder phone calls, send text messages, design bus ads, or work with religious leaders to get the message out that follow-up care is important. For a more in-depth look at new media, including types, who uses each type of media, and their relative strengths and weaknesses, please see the New Media section in this chapter.

TAILORED AND/OR TARGETED MESSAGES

According to Hawkins, Kreuter, Resnicow, Fishbein, and Dijkstra (2008), "tailoring" refers to creating materials customized to a specific individual, whereas "targeting" refers to creating materials customized to a specific set of audience criteria. Messages can be tailored or targeted to a number of factors, such as demographics, stage of change, knowledge, attitude, or health literacy level. Tailored health messages require knowledge of an individual's characteristics, and will be specific to that individual. Tailoring and targeting materials can increase their effectiveness, though work is continuing to explore the best ways to do so.

LANGUAGES SPOKEN IN THE UNITED STATES

According to the U.S. Census Bureau, 2011 American Community Survey, Table 1, Detailed Languages Spoken at Home by English-Speaking Ability for the Population 5 year and over 2011 (Ryan, 2013), the top 20 languages spoken in the United States are

1. English only—230,947,071
2. Spanish—37,579,787
3. Chinese—2,882,497
4. Tagalog—1,594,413
5. Vietnamese—1,419,539
6. French—1,301,443
7. Korean—1,141,277
8. German—1,083,637
9. Arabic—951,699
10. Russian—905,843
11. Indic Languages other than Hindi, Urdu, Gujarati—815,345
12. French Creole—753,990

13. Italian—723,632
14. Portuguese—673,566
15. Hindi—648,983
16. Polish—607,531
17. Japanese—436,110
18. Persian—407,586
19. Urdu—373,851
20. Gujarati—358,422

SOCIAL MARKETING

Social marketing is a powerful but often misunderstood tool. Social marketing, as described by Lefebvre and Flora (1988), is the "design, implementation, and control of programs aimed at increasing the acceptability of a social idea, practice [or product] in one or more groups of target adopters. The process actively involves the target population, who voluntarily exchange their time and attention for help in meeting their health needs as they perceive them."

Social marketing borrows heavily from commercial marketing techniques, but aims to sell a healthy behavior rather than, say, toothpaste. Perhaps the most well-known concept from social marketing is that of the "four Ps": product, price, place, and promotion. Each concept is discussed in the following section with an example from the CDC's VERB campaign (CDC, 2010), a nationwide, multicultural social marketing campaign conducted between 2002 and 2006 and aimed at encouraging youth ages 9 to 13 to engage in physical activity daily.

- Product: In health education, the product is usually the health behavior targeted in the program you are offering, though it can also be an actual product as well. In the VERB campaign, the product was physical activity.

- Price: Often thought of as the cost to participate in the program, price in social marketing should be thought of much more broadly. What does it cost the customer to "buy" the product you are selling? In the case of the VERB campaign, the price of participating in physical activity can include the price of needed equipment (shoes, balls, swim suits, admission to pools, jump ropes, etc.) but also the more indirect costs of time (time being physically active cannot also be spent sleeping, doing homework, etc.), safety (the risk of injury), and possible emotional stress (losing, failing at learning a new activity, etc.). It is the goal of the social marketing campaign to convince the customer that these costs are lower than the cost of NOT performing the behavior (that there are costs to being inactive—say, being out of shape or missing out on playing with your friends who are being physically active) and to help the customer find ways to make the costs affordable. The VERB campaign made sure to include very low (financial) cost activities and gave away balls, jump ropes, and so on to keep customer costs manageable.

■ Place: Often in health education it is necessary to place messages where the behavior is to be performed. For example, when we get into our car and forget to put on the seat belt, the car usually makes a beeping noise to remind us to fasten our seat belt—which is more useful than, say, receiving a message reminding you to fasten your seat belt while you are at the grocery store. Social marketing techniques require a careful consideration of where the behavior needs to be performed and where the consumer needs to be supported in adopting the behavior. In the VERB campaign, messages were placed on TV, radio, websites, and in text messaging, as well as at schools, community events, and festivals—all "places" where tweens were.

■ Promotion: Promotion is probably the least understood of the four Ps. Often it is thought of as the advertising around a campaign, but it is better thought of as a collection of offerings—including advertising—designed to increase audience engagement with the target behavior. This can include giveaways of products necessary to perform the behavior, prizes, incentives, and so on. In the VERB campaign, promotions included giveaways such as turnkey kits for schools and community groups and balls and other sports equipment, but also activities at sponsored events, online spaces where tweens could upload videos of themselves, and contests and sweepstakes.

The essential tenets, according to Andreasen (1995), of social marketing are the following:

1. Consumer behavior is the bottom line.
2. Programs must be cost effective.

3. All strategies begin with the customer.

4. Interventions involve the 4 Ps: product, price, place, and promotion.

5. Market research is essential to designing, pretesting, and evaluating intervention programs.

6. Markets are carefully segmented.

7. Competition is always recognized.
   (Andreasen, 1995, p. 14).

MEDIA RELATIONS

Developing effective techniques to partner with the media will help health educators deliver content to their audiences. Health educators must understand the needs of members of the media and how to interact with them to make sure that everyone's needs can be best met. Successful partnerships are not only possible, but can be of substantial benefit to both parties.

Members of the media have unique needs that are not always obvious to the general public. They work on very tight deadlines—often a matter of hours—and often cover a huge range of topics, making it impossible for them to be an expert on every one. Therefore, journalists rely heavily on sources to make sure their stories accurately represent the situation. If, as health educators, we want health topics to be fairly and accurately reported in the media, we need to make sure that the members of the media who deliver these stories know where to get credible information quickly.

One technique health educators rely on to get stories to the media is the press release. Press releases are sent to journalists to try to generate interest in a story—a way of "selling" your story to the media. They are written in the third person and in a professional tone, conveying the "who, what, when, where, why, and how" of a story. This is one area in health communication where there is not a lot of room to be creative—the template is fixed and designed to help the journalist quickly understand a story and make a decision about whether it is a story he or she would like to pursue (see Sample Press Release)

Two areas aside from the template are of particular concern when writing a press release. The first is the opening—the title and first paragraph. Given that a single journalist sifts through hundreds of press releases in a week, your opening is critical—if the first few lines do not catch their attention, your press release is likely to end up in the recycling bin. It needs to be factual, engaging, and start to suggest a story of interest to the journalist's readers. To use a media term, it needs to "hook" the journalist. The other area in the press release that requires careful thought is the quotes. Think of them as a free sample of the quotes your organization can offer to the journalist. Understandable, relevant, and engaging quotes from a credible source (usually the president, executive director, or some high-ranking person in your organization) signal to the journalist that he or she is going to have access to a good source for the story, which would lend credence to his or her work.

SAMPLE PRESS RELEASE

Contact (Your Name)
(Your Telephone Number)
(Your Email)

(Date)
FOR IMMEDIATE RELEASE

CATCHY BUT PITHY HEADLINE HERE DESIGNED TO GARNER INTEREST
(CITY, STATE) Introduction sentence, which should contain the who, what, when, and where of the story.
Second sentence (paragraph), with supporting details about the event, topic, paper, and so on. Include or expound on the "why" of the story: Why should the journalist expect this would be of interest to their readers? Incidence, prevalence, and local angle go here.
"Soundbite quote," said the very important person involved with the story. "I'll give you an even pithier soundbite quote, so you know that you will get interesting, relevant quotes to publish in your story."
Additional information about the disease, cause, event, and so on.
"Soundbite quote," ideally from someone else in the organization or another organization who will also be interviewed for the story.

Tagline of organization, including mission, and contact information.

New Media and Other Innovative Tools

Communicating about health in the 21st century almost certainly will require an active knowledge of new media. Traditional media—newspapers, radio, television—have not been totally replaced, but are often in direct competition with newer forms of media enabled by technology. The Web 2.0 is a term that refers to websites that are interactive (rather than didactic), easy to use, scalable, and can perform in a variety of ways. According to Wikipedia (itself an example of Web 2.0 principles), "A Web 2.0 site may allow users to interact and collaborate with each other in a social media dialogue as creators of user-generated content in a virtual community, in contrast to websites, where people are limited to the passive viewing of content. Examples of Web 2.0 include social networking sites, blogs, wikis, folksonomies, video-sharing sites, hosted services, Web applications, collaborative consumption platforms, and mashups." (en.wikipedia.org/wiki/Web_2.0). In the following section, we review some of the most commonly used new media and highlight how they might be—or have been—used in health campaigns. The Pew Internet and American Life Project (www.pewinternet.org) has the latest statistics and figures on who is doing what on the Internet and should be a first step for health educators considering the Internet as a channel for message delivery.

Social Networking Sites, for example, Facebook, Twitter, Pinterest, Instagram, and Google+, offer users a way to interact with others who have common interests and/or social networks. They are among the most commonly used new media, boasting, in Facebook's case, over a billion registered users. Different populations tend to frequent different social media sites—women, for example, are much more frequent users of Pinterest than men, and African Americans and Latinos are overrepresented on Twitter or Instagram.

There are specific social media sites that may have relevance to a health educator, including:

Academia.edu—for academics and researchers

CafeMoms—for mothers

CaringBridge—for patients and caregivers of those with serious medical conditions

PatientsLikeMe—for patients with serious medical conditions

Internationally, there are many different social media sites, and some of the most popular in the United States may not even be available in other countries. As always, understanding your audience and knowing where they get their information and who they trust, is critical to good health communication.

Pros: Social media sites are popular, easy to use, and can reach a wide number of people. It is also possible to pay to advertise on many of them to target information to different demographics, say, women between 25 and 40 or men who live in the southeastern United States. Users often help to spread your message by retweeting, forwarding, or sharing messages. Social media channels also provide instant feedback from your audience in the forms of comments and activity. They are also easily evaluated for process measures—users usually have access to information about how many people have seen or interacted with a message.

Cons: It can be hard to know exactly who is getting your message, and you only have feedback from those who chose to give it. The 24/7 nature of these channels requires careful and nearly constant monitoring to ensure that comments posted are acceptable to the message sender and to ensure that the message is being received as intended.

Blogs: or weblogs are online journals that can be accessed by anyone with an Internet connection. They provide a more in-depth way to explore a topic, as they are not limited by number of characters. Blogs can be written by an individual or come from an organization and be authored by different people. They often include a comment section where readers can interact with the author and others.

Pros: A blog gives the author an unlimited amount of space to write. Blogs can easily accommodate different ways of communication by including videos, pictures, audio, links to other web pages, interactive formats, and so on. They are a good place for discussion or to teach or explain more complex information, and are often read by people with a deeper interest in the given topic who are looking for significant amounts of information.

Cons: Content has to be seen and considered interesting by readers to get them to read it. Competing for eyes with all the other information available out there is a challenge, especially in trying to engage readers with limited literacy skills or attention spans. Readers expect frequent updating, and developing content is a time-consuming task.

MOBILE TECHNOLOGIES

Mobile (or cell) phones are one of the fastest growing technologies in the world. According to the Pew Internet and American Life Survey (www.pewinternet.org), from January 2017, 95% of American adults own a cell phone and 77% own a smartphone. Cell phones and particularly smartphones are increasingly being used as ways to connect with users, be it through mobile apps (or applications [computer programs] that work specifically on a smartphone) for social networking sites; health apps, which can track physical activity, biometric information such as blood pressure or blood sugar levels, or other health information; or text messaging. Nearly 80% of Americans text message, and programs such as Text4Baby (www.text4baby) utilize text message functions to deliver timely, targeted health information to users.

CONCLUSION

Not all communication and education happens with members of the general public; sometimes, health educators are advocating at the organizational, local, state, or national level, using a variety of methods and channels. But the same broad strategies apply: having goals and objectives; understanding the topic and your audience; selecting appropriate strategies—be they trusted, familiar ones like press releases and letters to the editor or new ones like Facebook and Instagram—and having an evaluation plan.

That is it! You have made it through all Seven Areas of Responsibility. Next, it is time to put your knowledge to the test by, well, actually taking a (mock) test—in Chapter 9.

REVIEW QUESTIONS

1. A health educator has identified an emerging issue that is affecting the health of people in her community. She believes she needs to engage in advocacy with state lawmakers to change a policy that is exacerbating the health condition. What would be her next step?

    A. Gather information about the health topic from reliable resources.
    B. Set goals and objectives.
    C. Join a coalition of organizations and people interested in the health topic.
    D. Draft a letter to state lawmakers.

2. A health educator strategically uses the mass media as a resource for advancing social or public policy through the reframing of issues from a policy prospective. He or she is engaging in:

   A. Social marketing
   B. Media literacy
   — C. Media advocacy
   D. Electioneering

   product, price, place, promotion

3. In social marketing, this "P" is the behavior you are trying to get your audience to do, services you provide, or objects you offer:

   — A. Product
   B. Price
   C. Promotion
   D. Perceived benefit

4. In social marketing, this "P" is the communication messages, materials, channels, or activities you use to get your message to your audience:

   A. Product
   B. Price
   — C. Promotion
   D. Perceived benefit

5. When developing a health communication intervention, prioritizing target audience segment(s) allows you to:

   — A. Tailor messages for all segments.
   B. Avoid spreading your resources too thin.
   C. Address secondary audiences.
   D. Be certain that no group is left out.

6. A health educator working in a community center is developing a social media campaign to encourage seniors to be physically active. She has segmented her audience into three groups: inactive "Super Seniors" (those older than 80 years); active, younger, female seniors (65–75); and those who have recently reduced their activity after a health event. After matching each high-priority audience segment with current and desired behaviors, the next step is to narrow her audience/behavior pairs based on:

   A. The ability to identify an antecedent behavior
   B. The presence of a social determinant of health

    C. Risk, impact, behavioral, resource, and political feasibility
    D. The likelihood of creating a permanent lifestyle change

7. A major challenge of developing persuasive messages is

    A. They are inherently unethical.
    B. Identifying the most effective channel, context, and message content
    C. Finding enough statistics to make a convincing argument
    D. The limited number of techniques that exist for evaluating the message's effectiveness

8. Which of the following is not directly involved in the organizing, financing, and implementation of health-related policy?

    A. The media
    B. Congress
    C. Healthcare providers
    D. Local communities

9. How many hours of continuing education does a Certified Health Education Specialist (CHES®) have to earn every 5 years to maintain his or her credential?

    A. 45
    B. 55
    C. 65
    D. 75

10. Which of the following is least likely to be true?

    A. Using plain language is desirable in communicating with the public.
    B. Communicating facts clearly to the public is more important than communicating clearly to professionals.
    C. Using plain language is desirable in communicating to an academic audience.
    D. Tailoring your message to your audience will improve your communication.

11. All channels of communication have their advantages and disadvantages. Which of the following channels is most likely to have credibility and access among its chief limitations?

    A. Television
    B. Blogs

C. Newspapers

D. Peer-reviewed journals

12. A health educator has determined, through a review of the literature, holding several focus groups, and collecting surveys from the population of interest, that lobbying is necessary to create a new law that will protect the public's health. What should the next step be?

A. Begin planning an advocacy campaign.

B. Hold public meetings to rally support for changing the law.

C. Check his or her workplace's policy on advocacy activities.

D. Hold a press conference.

13. All of the following are advantages of using television as a channel for communicating health information except

A. Can reach low-income audiences

B. It has the largest audience reach

C. It is flexible and inexpensive

D. Messages can be controlled

14. Approximately what percentage of Americans are considered "proficient" in terms of health literacy?

A. 2%

B. 12%

C. 22%

D. 32%

15. Which of the following is not a strategy for creating readable materials?

A. Keep sentences short.

 – B. Use the passive voice.

C. Use headings and subheadings.

D. Justify the left margin.

16. Which of the following is most likely to state reliable, unbiased health information?

A. An article in a popular magazine

B. A brochure from a health foods company

C. A website from a pharmaceutical company

D. A peer-reviewed journal article

17. The following are important components of health literacy except

    A. Cultural competency
    B. Ability to navigate systems
    C. Functional literacy
    D. Innate intelligence

18. A social worker at a hospital has developed a packet of information and a list of resources for families of people struggling with addiction. He wants to make sure that the information and resources are understandable and helpful to families. Rank in order, from most helpful to least helpful, the activities below that he could use to understand if his information and resources will be helpful to the families he is trying to reach:

1. Hold several focus groups or formalized testing with families of people with addiction to drugs or alcohol to discuss the materials and receive feedback.
2. Show the materials to a couple of families as he encounters them in the course of his duties, and solicit feedback.
3. Show them to coworkers who have knowledge of the target population, and solicit their feedback.
4. Use the reading-level analyzer on his word-processing software and revise until the level is at eighth grade or below.
5. Do nothing.

    A. 1, 2, 3, 4, 5
    B. 2, 1, 3, 4, 5
    C. 5, 4, 3, 2, 1
    D. 2, 1, 5, 4, 3

19. A health educator is tracking how many trainings her staff has conducted and how many copies of educational materials they have sent out as part of campaign to ensure that children with asthma are being identified and treated. What type of evaluation are these activities?

    A. Formative
    B. Process
    C. Outcome
    D. Impact

20. How many Americans have basic or below basic levels of health literacy?

    A. 7 million
    B. 27 million
    C. 47 million
    D. 77 million

ANSWERS

1. A. Gather information about the health topic from reliable resources

After identifying a health topic, the second step in engaging the advocacy process is to gather information about the health topic from reliable resources. These can include peer-reviewed journals, federal or state repositories of vital statistics, reputable nongovernmental organization (NGO) sources, or primary data.

2. C. Media advocacy

Media advocacy is the process by which mass media is used to influence or advance public policy. **Media literacy** is the ability to access, analyze, evaluate, and create **media**, so while media literacy would be necessary for media advocacy, it would not be sufficient. Social marketing is a technique through which program planners utilize the four "Ps" of marketing to bring about behavior change, whereas electioneering is to take part in the activities of a campaign.

3. A. Product

The product is the target behavior you are trying to get your audience to adopt or maintain. It can also be an object or service you are implementing as part of your program. In the Truth Campaign to End Youth Smoking, the product was feeling rebellious, in control, and "cool" by attacking adults who try to manipulate teens into smoking.

4. C. Promotion

Promotion is the messages, channels, or activities you use to get your audience to adopt the target behavior. These can include traditional TV, social media, radio spots, brochures, posters, and so on, or objects they can use when performing the behavior, such as water bottles for encouraging physical activity. In the Truth Campaign, the promotion included TV, Internet, and billboard ads with messages that appealed to youth's desire to be in control and oppositional to adult authority figures with questionable motives.

5. B. Avoid spreading your resources too thin

Prioritizing target audiences allows you to use program resources where they will be most effective.

6. C. Risk, impact, behavioral, resource, and political feasibility

In deciding what segments of the audience to target for intervention, a health educator must examine what health risks each segment faces, how likely it is that "the needle can be moved" on the population (some populations are easier to change than others), the resources available to implement a change, and how acceptable an intervention is going to be politically and to the population. All of these decisions go into planning which segments of the population are going to receive attention and resources and which are lower priority, either because of need or because they are too difficult or expensive to work with.

7. B. Identifying the most effective channel, context, and message content

Evaluations have shown that persuasive messages can be very effective at changing behavior and can be done ethically. And certainly for a variety of topics, there is a wealth of statistics available, though presenting people with statistics is not always very persuasive (we all know that tobacco kills thousands upon thousands of people a year, yet many Americans still smoke). Finding the right mix of channels, places and times, and content of messages that will ultimately change people's behaviors is an enduring problem for creating persuasive messages, since one mix may be effective for some audience members but not for others.

8. A. The media

The media may be a conduit through which policies are advocated for, and communicated through, but they do not directly affect the creation and delivery of health policy.

9. D. 75

National Commission for Health Education Credentialing, Inc. (NCHEC) requires academic preparation specifically in health education, passing of the written exam, and 75 hours of continuing education every 5 years.

10. B. Communicating facts clearly to the public is more important than communicating clearly to professionals

Material should be communicated clearly to any audience, regardless if the audience is comprised of professionals or the general public.

11. B. Blogs

Electronic media do many things well, but divides still remain in terms of access, and the credibility of electronic media can be harder to establish.

12. C. Check his or her workplace's policy on advocacy activities
Federal, state, and organizational laws and policies may prohibit lobbying by organizations. A health educator should know what the rules for lobbying are before embarking on a lobbying campaign.

13. C. It is flexible and inexpensive
Unless it is free media (such as an interview on a news program), television is a very expensive medium. Because of high production and airtime costs, a limited number of messages can be created and shown.

14. B. 12%
Only 12% of Americans are in the "proficient" category.

15. B. Use the passive voice
Keeping sentences short, using headings, judicious use of white space, and justifying the left margin (not centered or right-justified text) as people are used to reading, all help increase readability. The use of the passive voice generally creates extra words to read and can confuse readers as to your meaning (such as in this sentence!).

16. D. A peer-reviewed journal article
While all can be interesting and possibly appropriate sources of information, the information gained from a peer-reviewed journal article is most likely to be accurate, reliable, and unbiased. However, mistakes and even bias do happen in the peer-reviewed literature as well, which is why we consider the preponderance of evidence there and not just the findings of individual studies.

17. D. Innate intelligence
Health literacy is "the degree to which individuals have the capacity to obtain, process, and understand basic health information and services needed to make appropriate health decisions." Health literacy is dependent on both individual ability and systematic factors, including a person's ability to read (functional literacy), and do math (numeracy), navigate the healthcare system, and navigate culture. It does not dependent on innate intelligence—many highly intelligent people have low levels of health literacy.

18. A. 1, 2, 3, 4, 5

In a perfect world, you would be able to hold a series of focus groups (or formalized testing if confidentiality is a concern) and really test the materials with family members of people with addiction to drugs or alcohol. Materials are made better with thorough testing, revision, and retesting. However, in the real world, we often lack time and resources for such testing, so an alternative such as asking (in a professionally appropriate way) for feedback from members of a culture may have to substitute for formal testing.

19. B. Process

Monitoring and evaluating the implementation of a campaign is process evaluation.

20. D. 77 million

More than a third of adults were in the basic (47 million) and below basic (30 million) health literacy groups. These adults can read a pamphlet or a short list of instructions, respectively, but may not be able to read and understand instructions on a prescription label.

REFERENCES

Agency for Healthcare Research and Quality. (2015). Use the teach-back method: tool #5. Retrieved from https://www.ahrq.gov/professionals/quality-patient-safety/quality-resources/tools/literacy-toolkit/healthlittoolkit2-tool5.html

American Public Health Association. (2017). Top 10 rules for advocacy. Retrieved from https://www.apha.org/policies-and-advocacy/advocacy-for-public-health/coming-to-dc/top-ten-rules-of-advocacy

Andreasen, A. R. (1995). *Marketing social change: Changing behavior to promote health, social development, and the environment*. San Francisco, CA: Jossey-Bass.

Centers for Disease Control and Prevention. (2010). Youth media campaign: VERB, it's what we do. Retrieved from http://www.cdc.gov/youthcampaign

Hawkins, R. P., Kreuter, M., Resnicow, K., Fishbein, M., & Dijkstra, A. (2008). Understanding tailoring in communicating about health. *Health Education Research, 23*(3), 454–466. doi:10.1093/her/cyn004

Lefebvre, R. C., & Flora, J. A. (1988). Social marketing and public health intervention. *Health Education Quarterly, 15*, 299–315. doi:10.1177/109019818801500305

National Center for Education Statistics. (2006). The health literacy of America's adults: Results from the 2003 National Assessment of adult literacy . Washington, DC: U.S. Department of Education.

Pew Internet and American Life. (2017, January). Cell phone and smartphone ownership demographics. Retrieved from http://www.pewinternet.org/data-trend/mobile/cell-phone-and-smartphone-ownership-demographics

Ryan, C. (2013). Detailed languages spoken at home by English-speaking ability for the population 5 years and over: 2011 (Table 1). In *Language use in the United States: 2011* (ACS-22, p. 3). Retrieved from https://www.census.gov/prod/2013pubs/acs-22.pdf

U.S. Department of Health and Human Services. (2010). *Healthy people 2020*. Washington, DC: U.S. Government Printing Office.

Chapter 9

Sample CHES® Exam

In this chapter, you find 165 sample test questions from each of the Seven Areas of Responsibility in the expected proportion of an actual exam. Answers with identification of related competency will follow the exam. In the CHES® exam, 150 of the questions will be counted toward your score and 15 of the questions will be trial questions for potential use in future exams; you will not, of course, know which are the "real" questions. Try taking the sample exam in this chapter in circumstances similar to the CHES® exam by timing yourself and completing it in one sitting; can you do it in less than 3 hours?

1. A team of researchers conducts an investigation into whether small incentives can encourage older adults to stop smoking. They publish their findings in a peer-reviewed journal. A newspaper then runs an article about their published findings. Using this scenario, please answer the following questions:

   The journal article is a _____ source:

   A. Primary
   B. Secondary
   C. Tertiary
   D. Quaternary

2. The newspaper article is an example of a _____ source:

   A. Primary
   B. Secondary
   C. Tertiary
   D. Quaternary

3. Preparing for a program launch may include all of the following activities EXCEPT:

   A. Hiring and training staff.
   B. Issuing requests for proposals (RFPs) and awarding funds.
   C. Analyzing focus group data.
   D. Producing materials.

4. A logic model can convey the purpose of an initiative, show why it is important, provide a common reference point to all involved, and:

   A. Show funding sources.
   B. Identify expected outcomes.
   C. Enumerate planned activities.
   D. Change underlying assumptions.

5. Phase 1 of PRECEED–PROCEED includes all of the following EXCEPT:

   A. Articulating the community's needs and desires.
   B. Considering the community's problem-solving capacity.
   C. Identifying strengths and resources.
   D. Considering enabling factors.

6. Which of the following is true of Figure 9.1?

   A. Negatively skewed
   B. Positively skewed
   C. Symmetrical
   D. A and B

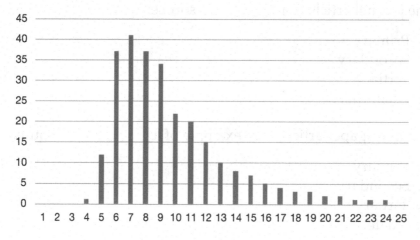

Figure 9.1.

7. Common elements of a program proposal include an abstract, project plan, budget, and:

   A. Specific aims.
   B. SMART aims.
   C. Letters of support.
   D. A and C.

SCENARIO for QUESTIONS 8 and 9: A health educator is approached by a technology company about implementing its program, which uses tablets to deliver educational content to seniors in their homes to reduce social isolation and loneliness.

8. What would be the first question the health educator should consider before adopting the technology into the intervention?

   A. Is there funding available to offset the cost of the technology?
   B. How much training time will staff need to learn the technology?
   C. Will the technology be acceptable to or wanted by the population?
   D. Will the organization be perceived as innovative if it adopts the technology?

9. In this project, the app has provisions for those with loss of vision or hearing to enable them to participate in the program. Additionally, the program does not require seniors to leave their homes, so it is inclusive of those who have physical limitations that make travel difficult. These tablets are also being provided at little or no cost to low-income seniors. These accommodations are examples of what ethical principle?

   A. Beneficence
   B. Transparency
   C. Confidentiality
   D. Equity

10. In writing an evaluation report to a funding agency, which of the following is NOT recommended?

   A. Clearly state the strengths and limitations of the evaluation.
   B. Describe stakeholders and their roles.
   C. Use technical jargon.
   D. Use illustrations, examples, and stories.

11. According to Bloom's Taxonomy, which classification of skills includes the ability to define, describe, label, or state?

    A. Comprehension
    B. Knowledge
    C. Application
    D. Evaluation

12. <u>Jane Doe, PhD, Principal Investigator</u> (effort = 3 calendar months). Dr. Doe will be responsible for the overall coordination and supervision of all aspects of the study, including hiring, training, and supervising staff/students; recruiting study participants; coordinating treatment and assessment components; scheduling and staff assignments; and data management. Additionally, she will conduct the training sessions, assist with statistical analyses, and be responsible for reporting the project's findings.

    This is an example of a:

    A. Job description
    B. Performance review
    C. Study plan
    D. Budget justification

13. Creating messages specifically aimed at an individual based on his or her particular characteristics is called

    A. Cultural competency
    B. Drafting
    C. Tailoring
    D. Personalizing

14. In the United States, what is the name of the organization often charged with reviewing research study or intervention designs?

    A. Intervention Design Review
    B. Institutional Review Board
    C. Intervention Review Board
    D. Intervention Review Committee

15. A health educator tasked with reducing motor vehicle accidents discovers that federal funds have been made available to add bike lanes to major roads. These funds would be an example of what kind of factor?

    A. Predisposing
    B. Reinforcing
   ~**C.** Enabling
    D. Institutional

16. All of the following are important in creating readable materials EXCEPT:

    A. Avoid or define jargon.
    B. Use a lot of white space.
    C. Focus on improving knowledge rather than changing behavior.
    D. Use headings and subheads.

17. A _____contains inputs, activities, outputs, and outcomes.

    A. Strategic plan
    B. SMART objective
    C. Logic model
    D. Ecological model

18. Which of the following is the correct order of the PROCEED model for public health planning?

    A. Implementation, process evaluation, impact evaluation, outcome evaluation
    B. Implementation, impact evaluation, process evaluation, outcome evaluation
    C. Process evaluation, implementation, impact evaluation, outcome evaluation
    D. Formative evaluation, implementation, outcome evaluation, impact evaluation

19. A health education specialist encounters a client with his family in the local grocery store. While they are all talking the educator asks the client how he is responding to his diabetes medication. The health educator has violated which of the following of the responsibilities of the Health Education Profession's *Code of Ethics*?

    A. Nonmaleficence
    B. Confidentiality

C. Informed consent

D. Autonomy

20. An important distinction between program evaluation and research is that evaluation:

A. Is always more expensive

B. Is not intended to be generalizable to a wider population

C. Is easier to do

D. Is more useful

21. Which one of the following is the correct rank for heart disease as a cause of mortality for individuals between the ages of 45 and 54 in the United States in 2010?

A. First

B. Second

C. Third

D. Fourth

22. Which one of the following interventions is the best example of primary prevention?

A. Mammography

B. Physical therapy

C. Tracheostomy

D. Immunization

SCENARIO for QUESTIONS 23 and 24: A heath education specialist is designing a program for residents in a low-income area. A needs assessment has shown those residents have lower-than-average rates of annual flu vaccination. The educator decides to hold a flu shot clinic, and residents who get a flu shot will be given $500.

23. This incentive could be called into question because it could be considered:

A. Coercive

B. Culturally insensitive

C. Discriminatory

D. Cost-effective

24. In this scenario, the educator would be violating which of the following responsibilities for health education practice?

    A. Financial
    B. Moral
    C. Legal
    D. Ethical

25. _____**statistics** make predictions about a population based on a sample of data taken from the population in question.

    A. Inferential
    B. Descriptive
    C. Experimental
    D. Applied

26. Logic models can be constructed:

    A. Right-to-left only
    B. Left-to-right or right-to-left
    C. Left-to-right only
    D. From the bottom up

27. Which of the following aims to find evidence of disease early to reduce morbidity and mortality?

    A. Primary prevention
    B. Secondary prevention
    C. Tertiary prevention
    D. Quaternary prevention

28. When interviewing a potential new hire, which of the following should the person in charge of the hiring process ask the applicant?

    A. Qualifying degrees and/or certifications
    B. Health status
    C. Working style
    D. A and C

29. Voting registration drives and developing a press release in support of a bill are examples of:

    A. Advocacy strategies
    B. Grassroots advocacy only

    C. Media advocacy only

    D. Unethical behavior

30. The duration of the study, the potential risks and benefits, and the requirements of the study are all pieces of information necessary for:

    A. SMART objectives

    B. Record reviews

    C. The Belmont Report

    D. Informed consent

31. Periodic data collection to ensure that programs are being implemented as they were intended is called:

    A. Correlation study

    B. Outcome evaluation

    C. Fidelity monitoring

    D. Input monitoring

32. Which of the following is an example of a learning objective?

    A. The community nurse educator will demonstrate the correct use of a blood pressure cuff.

    B. The group facilitator will explain two benefits of medication adherence.

    C. The principals will participate in a trauma-informed teaching workshop.

    D. The conference attendee will be able to demonstrate how to perform cardiopulmonary resuscitation (CPR).

33. The Belmont Report outlines three human-subject protection guidelines: beneficence, respect for persons, and:

    A. Fairness

    B. Nonmaleficence

    C. Justice

    D. Cultural sensitivity

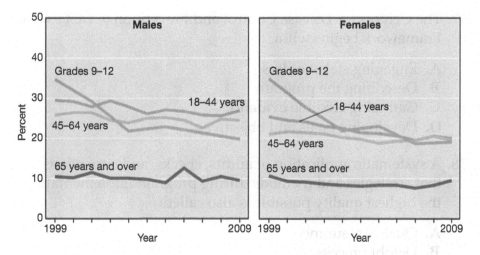

Figure 9.2. Cigarette smoking among students in Grades 9 through 12 and adults age 18 and older, by sex, grade, and age, in the United States, 1999 through 2009.

34. According to Figure 9.2, in 2001, which of the following was true:

   A. The smoking rate for male children and adults aged 18 to 44 was essentially the same.
   B. Seniors' rates of smoking increased dramatically over the previous year.
   C. In the 45 to 64 age group, a higher percentage of women smoked when compared to men.
   D. Rates of smoking in high school girls was at its highest point.

35. According to Figure 9.2, during the period of 2005 to 2009, seniors experienced:

   A. Universally declining rates of smoking
   B. A brief uptick in smoking rates in males, followed by a return to baseline
   C. A sharp increase in smoking across the board
   D. The lowest rates of smoking recorded by women in 2009

36. According to Figure 9.2, who had the lowest rate of smoking in 2007?

   A. Men over the age of 65
   B. Women age 18 to 44
   C. Women over the age of 65
   D. Men age 18 to 44

37. The Centers for Disease Control and Prevention (CDC) Evaluation Framework begins with:

    A. Engaging stakeholders
    B. Describing the program
    C. Gathering credible evidence
    D. Developing goals and objectives

38. A systematic application of audits, checks, and corrections to ensure that strategies and methods during program implementation are of the highest quality possible is also called:

    A. Quality assurance
    B. Delphi process
    C. Program evaluation
    D. Internal affairs

39. When designing health communication campaigns, which is the correct order to plan and implement a campaign?

    A. Assess needs, write goals/objectives, choose channel(s), implement, evaluate
    B. Write goals/objectives, assess needs, chose channel(s), implement, evaluate
    C. Assess needs, choose channel(s), write goals/objectives, implement, evaluate
    D. Choose channel(s), assess needs, write goals/objectives, implement, evaluate

40. SMOG, Flesch–Kincaid, and FOG are all examples of tools to assess:

    A. Cultural competence
    B. Central tendency
    C. Reading level
    D. Kurtosis

41. "In the next two years, there will be a 30% increase in the number of new parents who say they intend to vaccinate their babies on time" is an example of a:

    A. Program goal
    B. Learning objective
    C. Educational objective
    D. Behavioral objective

42. _____ reflects a measurement tool's ability to measure a variable consistently and _____ reflects a measurement's tool to measure what it is supposed to measure.

    A. Reliability/validity
    B. Validity/reliability
    C. Validity/variation
    D. Variation/reliability

43. The type of evaluation that measures whether a health education intervention has caused a desired change in a population of interest is called:

    A. Formative
    B. Process
    C. Educational
    D. Summative

44. Perceived severity, perceived susceptibility, and perceived benefits are all constructs in which theory or model?

    A. Theory of Reasoned Action
    B. Theory of Planned Behavior
    C. Transtheoretical Model
    – D. Health Belief Model

45. When conducting in-person trainings, which is a technique for assessing whether the participants learned the skill you were teaching?

    A. Call Back
    B. Teach-Back
    C. Scribner's Method
    D. Call and Response

46. Flip charts, site visits, PowerPoint presentations, and movies are all examples of what kind of media?

    A. Interactive
    B. Legal
    C. Educational
    D. Persuasive

47. A health education specialist is designing a social media campaign to increase breastfeeding initiation in young women of color. The best group to work with to design, pretest, and refine messages would be:

    A. Pediatricians
    B. High school teachers
    C. Public health nurses
    D. Young women of color

48. Cultural competency, the ability to navigate systems, and functional literacy are all components of:

    A. Numeracy
    B. Health literacy
    C. SMOG
    D. Cultural literacy

49. A food bank provides funding to local food vendors to enable them to provide fresh produce to residents in a food desert. Which of the following would be considered a medium-term outcome for this project?

    A. Patrons purchase more fresh fruits and vegetables.
    B. The vendor tracks the number of fresh produce items offered.
    C. The rate of diabetes is reduced in the community.
    D. Participants say Tuesdays are the best days for the vendors to sell fresh produce.

50. A person who has been exercising regularly for 2 weeks would be considered in which stage of the Transtheoretical Model?

    A. Precontemplation
    B. Contemplation
    C. Action
    D. Maintenance

51. Which of the following databases is designed for the public, rather than health professionals?

    A. Healthfinder.gov
    B. National Center for Health Statistics
    C. Medline
    D. ERIC

52. One way that program monitoring differs from other kinds of evaluation efforts, such as outcome evaluation studies, is that program monitoring is:

    A. Optional
    B. Continuous throughout the program
    C. Quantitative
    D. Theory-driven

53. A health education specialist working at a university implements a campaign to reduce underage drinking. The campaign is focused on changing the perception that all college students binge drink on the weekend and instead communicating that most college students do not drink or drink moderately on the weekend. This campaign is based on which construct from Social Cognitive Theory?

    A. Social norms
    B. Self-efficacy
    C. Observational learning
    D. Situation

54. A broad, future-oriented statement reflecting an aspirational aim of a program or organization is called a:

    A. SMART objective
    B. Goal
    C. Mission statement
    D. Vision statement

55. In a logic model, "staff," "funding," and "a swimming pool" would be considered:

    A. Outcomes
    B. Activities
    C. Inputs
    D. Outputs

56. In a logic model, the creation of "swimming classes" and "a website for participants to log the number of hours they swim" would be a considered:

    A. Outcomes
    B. Assumptions

    C. Inputs

    D. Outputs

57. Which of the following is true about program goals and objectives?

    A. Program participants should have the final say in determining them.

    B. They should be determined at the beginning of the planning process.

    C. They may be altered to better fit evaluation data.

    D. They can be better determined once implementation occurs.

58. Which of the following is NOT a framework for program evaluation:

    A. Reach

    B. RE-AIM

    C. PRECEED–PROCEED

    D. EBMR

59. A _____ is the amount that can be completely attributed to the activities of a particular project:

    A. Budget

    B. Direct cost

    C. Indirect cost

    D. Depreciation

60. In developing a campaign to get men to see their primary care physicians for regular health screenings, you find that their wives are often the ones who make their husband's doctor appointments. You decide to speak to a local women's group on the importance of men's healthcare. In this case, which kind of audience are the women?

    A. Primary

    B. Secondary

    C. Tertiary

    D. Quaternary

61. When collecting primary data, which of the following survey methods is likely to be the most expensive?

    A. In-person interview

    B. Telephone-based survey

C. Mail-based survey

D. Social media-based survey

62. A woman is considering quitting smoking but is very sure that if she does so, she will gain weight. A health educator using the Theory of Planned Behavior would have to influence which construct to address this concern?

   A. Perceived behavioral control
   B. Subjective norm
   C. Behavioral intention
 ~ D. Attitude

63. The Centers for Disease Control and Prevention's (CDC) Framework for Program Evaluation's final step is:

   A. Using and sharing results
   B. Justifying conclusions
   C. Describing the problem
   D. Engaging stakeholders

64. If a health problem is highly changeable and highly important to the population, which strategy should a health education specialist employ?

   A. Health education
   B. Social marketing
   C. Legal interventions
   D. Incentives

65. A Gantt chart would most likely be developed in what phase of program implementation?

   A. Program evaluation
   B. Enactment of the plan
   C. Establishment of a program management system
   D. Ending or sustaining the plan

66. All of the following are important concepts in social marketing EXCEPT:

   A. Consumer research
   B. Comprehensiveness
   C. Cost-effectiveness
   D. Competition

67. A health educator is hired to lobby Congress to raise taxes on junk food and use the revenue to lower the price of fruits and vegetables. Which form of communication would be most likely to gain the desired outcome?

   A. Face-to-face meetings
   B. Social media
   C. Letters
   D. Conference calls

68. A health education specialist who can identify, articulate, and translate an understanding of the mission, vision, values, beliefs, and ethics of an organization is exhibiting:

   A. Visionary leadership
   B. Sense of mission
   C. Understanding of political competencies
   D. Social dynamics

69. Which database is most likely to help a health educator looking for information about how nurses can help improve breastfeeding in rural areas?

   A. CINAHL
   B. MEDLINE
   C. HEDIR
   D. HEALTHPROM

70. A good data analysis and reporting plan will:

   A. Outline how the data for each monitoring and evaluation question will be coded.
   B. Describe how conclusions will be justified, how stakeholders will be kept informed, and when activities will be implemented.
   C. Plan for how monitoring and evaluation narratives will tell the same story.
   D. A and B

SCENARIO for QUESTIONS 71 and 72: A review of vital records shows a worrisome uptick in fatal car accidents. Upon further research, it is revealed that a high proportion of fatal car crashes involve drivers playing a new type of game on their smart phone while driving. A needs assessment shows that most people have never considered the particular risk of this behavior, and news has not spread of the number of crashes it caused.

71. What would be the first intervention a health educator should try to reduce the number of people playing this new game while driving?

   A. Education
   B. Social marketing
   C. Fear campaign
   D. Legislation

72. What would be the type of intervention a health educator might advocate after a variety of educational and persuasive techniques showed little impact on lowering the number of drivers still playing the game, and causing car crashes?

   A. Education
   B. Social marketing
   C. Fear campaign
   D. Legislation

73. Strategic plans seek to answer all of the following questions EXCEPT:

   A. Where do we want to be?
   B. Where are we now?
   C. Who is our competition?
   D. How do we get to where we want to be?

74. After convening a group, identifying necessary data, and completing a SWOT analysis, what is the next step for developing a strategic plan?

   A. Implement Year One plans.
   B. Prioritize strategies for the next 5 years.
   C. Decide evaluation strategy.
   D. Identify key stakeholders.

75. Which of the following helps planners conduct a situational analysis?

   A. HEDIR
   B. ERIC
   C. SWOT
   D. PATCH

76. Whether there is evidence for program activities leading to desired outcomes, whether the program addressed stakeholder concerns, and what level of noise the program generated are all questions that might be asked during what kind of program evaluation?

    A. Formative
    B. Monitoring
    C. Process
    D. Outcome

77. The 'M' in SMART objective stands for:

    A. Manageable
    B. Measurable
    C. Maximizing
    D. Malleable

78. What are the "4 Ps" of social marketing?

    A. Planning, price, people, and products
    B. People, place, package, and produce
    C. Product, price, place, and promotion
    D. Planning, package, people, and price

79. According to the diffusion of innovations theory, which of the following groups of people are the first to adopt a behavior?

    A. Laggards
    B. Early adopters
    C. Innovators
    D. Early majority

80. A student health program at a large university has hired a health educator to propose a health promotion program. The first thing the health educator should do is:

    A. Talk to students about their health concerns.
    B. Develop goals and objectives to reduce drinking.
    C. Use the trans theoretical model to stage student's readiness to change.
    D. Develop evaluation metrics.

81. _____ is the activity by which a person with specialized knowledge and skills is paid to help another person or organization make better decisions or plans.

   A. Consulting
   B. Training
   C. Teaching
   D. Researching

82. Perceived threat of a disease, perceived barriers, and cues to action are all constructs from which theory or model?

   A. Theory of Planned Behavior
   B. Theory of Reasoned Action
   C. Health Belief Model
   D. Ecological Model

83. In a SWOT analysis, opportunities, and threats are:

   A. Within your control
   B. Outside your control
   C. What your audience is doing
   D. What your partners are doing

84. The 'S' in SWOT analysis stands for:

   A. SMART objectives
   B. Strengths
   C. Systems
   D. Schedules

85. Which of the following is the correct order of steps to take to develop a focus group?

   A. Determine the focus group questions to be asked> Determine the objectives of the focus group> Recruit participants> Determine a data analysis plan
   B. Determine the objectives of the focus group> Determine the focus group questions to be asked> Recruit participants> Determine a data analysis plan
   C. Determine the objectives of the focus group> Recruit participants> Determine the focus group questions to be asked> Determine a data analysis plan

D. Determine the objectives of the focus group> Determine the focus group questions to be asked> Determine a data analysis plan> Recruit participants

86. Which of the following is NOT a limitation of survey data?

   A. Closed-ended questions may have lower validity
   B. Lack of context
   C. Geographical limitations
   D. Social-desirability bias

87. An owner of a medium-sized manufacturing plant is interested in beginning a worksite health promotion program. Which of the following is a true statement about using focus groups to develop a needs assessment?

   A. A focus group will give you highly generalizable data from which to base your program planning decisions.
   B. Focus groups should consist of approximately eight to 10 employees and should be have an assortment of management and labor to get a full understanding of employee opinions.
   C. The final report of information gathered in focus groups should not be shared back to the participants to preserve confidentiality.
   D. Even if you design, recruit, and analyze your focus groups well, you may need additional needs assessment information.

88. Data that are sorted into categories (such as gender) are considered what type of data?

   A. Ratio
   B. Nominal
   C. Interval
   D. Rank-order

89. Which of the following is a document which indicated shared interest and broadly lays out an intended common line of action, but is not legally binding?

   A. MOA
   B. MOU
   C. Cooperative agreement
   D. Partnership pledge

90. In the social ecological model, social determinates of health include all but the following:

   A. Availability of resources
   B. Exposure to crime
   C. Quality schools
   D. Exposure to toxic substances

91. Lecture, brainstorming, coaching, debates, and role-playing are all examples of:

   A. Training simulations
   B. Teaching strategies
   C. Public speaking
   D. Peer review

92. A health educator would choose to employ a pretest-posttest evaluation strategy to asses _____ from a training?

   A. Participant's feelings about a training
   B. Transferability of skills
   C. Change in knowledge
   D. Reduction in morbidity

93. The first step in program planning is:

   A. Assessing existing health needs and problems
   B. Evaluating program objectives
   C. Analyzing a communication strategy
   D. Identifying populations

94. _____ is a way to monitor and ensure the correct operations and service deliveries are in place for a program to be implemented as planned.

   A. Process evaluation
   B. Formative evaluation
   C. Outcome evaluation
   D. Impact evaluation

95. The Hierarchy of Effects Model lists the steps through which behavior change happen in which order?

   A. Acquisition of skills, change in attitude, short-term retention of information, one-time performance of behavior, reinforcement of behavior, maintenance of behavior

B. Change of attitude, acquisition of skills, short-term retention of information, long-term retention of information, decision making, reinforcement of behavior, maintenance of behavior
C. Change of attitude, acquisition of skills, decision making, short-term retention of information, long-term retention of information, decision making, reinforcement of behavior, maintenance of behavior
D. Acquisition of skills, change in attitude, short-term retention of information, long-term retention of information, decision making, reinforcement of behavior, maintenance of behavior

96. The type of study that exposes some participants to an intervention and compares the results to a group of participants who have not had the intervention but are similar to the group who got the intervention is called:

A. Experimental
B. Cross-sectional
C. Ecological
D. Prospective cohort

97. When planning a program for a local nonprofit, which of the following should be most important to a health education specialist?

A. A similar program's evaluation data
B. State health department goals and objectives
C. Needs assessment data
D. BRFSS data

98. If a survey question measures what it is intended to measure it is:

A. Reliable
B. Skewed
C. Valid
D. Accurate

99. Which of the following would not be a consideration for assessing whether an intervention caused an outcome?

A. Dose-response
B. Strength of association
C. Biologic plausibility
D. Correlation

100. The data collection approach that often yields the most helpful information to program planners while balancing efficiency and generalizability with the ability to explore needs of subgroups within a population is:

A. Quantitative
B. Qualitative
C. Mixed methods
D. Secondary

101. Effective health communication messages should be all of the following EXCEPT:

A. Consistent
B. Clear
C. Credible
D. Capricious

102. A small nonprofit devoted to helping adults with mental disabilities live as independently as possible has decided to use volunteers to help drive program participants to work-training programs. Which of the following would be the most likely concern for using volunteer labor in this capacity?

A. The costs of training volunteers to transport participants in such a way as to satisfy liability concerns
B. The volunteers would know who was a participant in the program
C. Volunteers might get bored
D. Funders might not approve of using volunteers

103. An owner of a medium-sized manufacturing plant is interested in beginning a worksite health promotion program. Which of the following are likely to be of least interest to the owner when evaluating outcomes?

A. Direct measures of productivity
B. Time-frame for the realization of benefits
C. Employee leisure-time activities
D. Health insurance costs

104. The model or theory that *Healthy People 2020* describes as explaining the "interrelationships among . . . factors that determine individual and population health" is the:

    A. Ecological Model
    B. Theory of Planned Behavior
    C. Theory of Reasoned Action
    D. Health Belief Model

105. Which of the following is an example of qualitative data:

    A. Vital statistics
    B. In-depth interviews
    C. Pretests and postests
    D. Meta-analyses

106. The five broad categories, from most to least individual, common to ecological models are:

    A. Innate, intrapersonal interpersonal, institutional, federal, international
    B. Intrapersonal, interpersonal, neighborhood, organizational, state, federal
    C. Innate, intrapersonal, interpersonal, institutional, community, public policy
    D. Individual, workplaces, community, federal, international

107. The study design generally perceived as having the most convincing evidence that an intervention caused an outcome is:

    A. Case-control study
    B. Interrupted time series
    C. Direct observation
    D. Randomized control study

108. According to Gagne's Theory of Instruction, what is the first step in providing instruction?

    A. Gain attention
    B. Inform learners of the objectives
    C. Build on prior knowledge
    D. Assess performance

109. Which of the following is the most important group of individuals to have advising a health educator interested in reducing drunk driving in the Midwest?

  A. State legislators and their staff
  B. Young men who have been convicted of driving under the influence (DUI)
  C. Pastors, rabbis, and other clergy from local houses of worship
  D. Police

110. The Social-Ecological Model assumes that health and well-being are affected by _____ of multiple determinates including biology, behavior, the environment, and policy.

  A. Linkages
  B. Connections
  C. Communications
  D. Interactions

111. Which technique has been proven to be most effective in recruiting new volunteers for a program?

  A. Extending personal invitations through staff, stakeholders, or clients
  B. Finding those required to do community service
  C. Social media advertising
  D. Recruiting the volunteers of similar organizations

112. When creating readable materials, you should:

  A. Use headings
  B. Use a mix of passive and active voice
  C. Chunk information
  D. A and C

113. Data collected by a researcher for the sake of informing a specific project is called:

  A. Tertiary
  B. Primary
  C. Secondary
  D. Generalizable

114. A budget is composed of:

    A. Indirect costs only
    B. Direct, indirect, and in-kind donations
    C. Direct and indirect costs
    D. Direct costs only

115. Addressing a participant in communication materials by name, and including details specific to that individual's knowledge, attitudes, and preferences is an example of what kind of health communication?

    A. Mass
    B. Social
    C. Tailored
    D. Specific

116. Preparing for a large scale health education campaign—including conducting formative research, developing and testing materials, and preparing for implementation takes approximately how long?

    A. 1 month
    B. 3 months
    C. 6 months
    D. 12 months

117. Process indicators measure:

    A. The program's activities and outputs
    B. Whether the program is achieving the expected effect
    C. Whether there has been a change in health status
    D. How cost-effective the program was

118. Press releases should contain all of the following EXCEPT:

    A. Name and contact information
    B. Jargon or technical language
    C. Interesting quotes
    D. Information about the organization

119. A health education specialist is working with a high school science teacher to plan a lesson on preventing drunk driving before prom. The best source to search for information on school-based programs is:

    A. MEDLINE
    B. PsycINFO

C. HEDIR
D. ERIC

120. The first thing a health educator should do when beginning a needs assessment is:

A. Conduct a community analysis
B. Assess reinforcing factors
C. Understand the health literacy levels of the community
D. Determine project budget

121. Using volunteers and using paid staff to perform agency functions is similar in what way?

A. Both require time to recruitment and training
B. Cost
C. Recognition and rewards are important for retention
D. A and C

122. All of the following would be good techniques for a face-to-face meeting with a legislator except:

A. Have a specific, tailored message
B. Make sure everyone in the group speaks
C. Make an appointment
D. Leave a fact-sheet

123. Good examples of secondary data include all of the following except:

A. Vital records
B. BRFSS
C. Interviews
D. Bureau of Labor Statistics data

124. A _____ study involves a group of people from whom data are collected prospectively or can be gleaned from historical record.

A. Time-series
B. Case-control
C. Experimental
D. Cohort

125. What percentage of Americans has low health literacy?

    A. 20%
    B. 30%
    C. 40%
    D. 50%

126. Sources of quantitative data include all of the following except:

    A. Surveys
    B. Pretests and posttests
    C. Healthy People 2020
    D. Observations

127. A health educator is asked to write a literature review for a grant proposal his organization is submitting to develop a project to test local schools for environmental contaminants in local schools. Which one of the following should he NOT do in the literature review portion of the proposal?

    A. Build an argument for the program
    B. Demonstrate the relevance of the program
    C. Present epidemiologic data related to the issue under study
    D. Describe how they will measure variables in program

128. When communicating health information to a reluctant audience, an instructor would find which of the following to be the least important?

    A. Emphasize the instructor's education and experience
    B. Explain why the topic is important
    C. Explain the value of acquiring the new knowledge or skills
    D. Engage the learner through multiple teaching styles

129. A health educator is asked to present findings from a community needs assessment to a local church. Which would be the first thing he should do to prepare an effective presentation.

    A. Use presentation software
    B. Find out more about the audience
    C. Visit the space where he will be presenting
    D. Write learning objectives

130. A _____ is defined as a "statement that *defines* the expected goal of a curriculum, course, lesson or activity in terms of demonstrable skills or knowledge that will be acquired by a student as a result of instruction."

    A. Learning objective
    B. Behavioral objective
    C. SMART objective
    D. Program objective

131. A _____ is a trial run of a program in order to evaluate feasibility, time, cost, acceptability, and potential adverse events.

    A. Prelaunch
    B. Pretest
    C. Pilot project
    D. Fidelity test

132. An example of _____ would be starting a petition to request that speedbumps be installed to slow traffic while an example of _____ is contacting a member of Congress to solicit funds for a traffic study.

    A. Electioneering/direct advocacy
    B. Grassroots advocacy/direct advocacy
    C. Indirect advocacy/direct advocacy
    D. Electioneering/grassroots advocacy

133. According to Bloom's Taxonomy, which of the following verbs shows the highest level of skills?

    A. List
    B. Use
    C. Justify
    D. Analyze

134. An important difference between a theory and a model is that:

    A. Models are better for designing programs that have successful outcomes.
    B. A model can draw on a series of theories to help describe a problem in a specific context.

C. All the constructs from a theory must be used for the theory to work but a model can be applied more loosely.

D. A model is a set of interrelated constructs, definitions, and statements that present a systematic view of events.

135. The three main kinds of indicators program evaluation seeks to understand are:

A. Contributing, direct, and indirect
B. Process, outcome, impact
C. Simple, precise, and measurable
D. Specific, measurable, achievable

136. Someone who is learning new information is most likely to remember it when they have

A. Read it
B. Seen it
C. Heard about it and seen it
D. Done it and taught it to someone else

137. The last step in a community needs assessment should be:

A. Analyzing data gathered
B. Creating SMART objectives
C. Sharing and validating the needs that have been identified
D. Obtaining Behavioral Risk Factor Surveillance System (BRFSS) data

138. _____ is a practical process to help organizations develop and adapt products, services, and activities of the needs of the populations your program serves.

A. Strategic planning
B. Environmental review
C. Active listening
D. Creative briefing

139. When assessing the quality of online information, which of the following is the least important to ask?

A. Who is responsible for this site?
B. Is the information evidence-based?
C. Is the information up-to-date?
D. Is the information written in an active or passive voice?

140. Which of the following best describes a Delphi Panel Process?

  A. A group of four to 10 homogenous people discussing a potential change
  B. The use of structured questionnaires used to generate consensus in a group of experts
  C. A small group of people privately ranking available possibilities to decide which should be prioritized
  D. A statistical analysis of separate but similar data in order to determine statistical significance

141. Adults with low-health literacy levels are most likely to get their health information from which sources?

  A. Newspapers
  B. TV
  C. Facebook
  D. B and C

142. A _____ allows health educators to get feedback from participants about program materials.

  A. Pilot test
  B. Pretest
  C. Pilot project
  D. Posttest

143. Which age group has the highest percentage of people who use the Internet regularly?

  A. 18 to 29
  B. 30 to 49
  C. 50 to 64
  D. 65+

144. A health educator has planned an intervention that will ensure that families in a high-risk area for infant death have safe sleeping areas for their babies. She plans to visit homes where babies are expected to make sure they have cribs set up and the environment is safe. She is concerned that parents may be resistant to having her come into their homes, despite having been told in several focus groups with pregnant mothers from the community that they would be interested in such a program and developing relationship

with several community gatekeepers. What should she do before launching the program?

A. Hold more focus groups
B. Do a literature search to get more information on safe sleep
C. Launch a pilot project in one neighborhood
D. Focus on something else

145. The Epidemiological Model for needs assessment asks all of the following questions except:

A. Who had the problem?
B. What is the problem?
C. What will solve the problem?
D. Why do those with the problem have it?

146. Common sources of secondary data include all of the following except:

A. Morbidity and Mortality Weekly Reports
B. BRFSS
C. NHANES
D. CINAHL

147. A school board is selecting a sexual health education curriculum to implement in ninth grade. Which is the least important issue for them to consider?

A. Cost
B. If students will be embarrassed by the curriculum
C. If parents support the curriculum
D. Feedback of other school districts about the competing curriculum

148. All of the following are techniques to help promote learning except:

A. Facilitate discussions rather than just lecture
B. Avoid repetition
C. Move from simple to complex ideas
D. Explain to the learners why the information is important

149. A health educator is working on a project investigating childhood asthma in a public school system in a metropolitan school district. After obtaining Institutional Review Board (IRB) and parental

approval, she randomly samples students from across the school district and asks them questions about their asthma and treatment. She finds that among those who have been diagnosed with asthma, 70% do not have their asthma medication available to them at all times during the day at school. This type of study is:

A. Time-series
B. Case-control
C. Ecological
D. Cross-sectional

150. In a school district that has struggled with low vaccination rates due to parental resistance and preferences for "natural" treatments, an unvaccinated child becomes sick with the measles. The school board decides to hire a health educator to launch a campaign to promote vaccinations for school-aged children. This is an example of:

A. A teachable moment
B. Coercive behavior
C. Incentives
D. A pilot study

151. A _____ is defined as a "statement of what students ought to be able to do as a consequence of instruction."

A. Behavioral objective
B. Attitudinal objective
C. SMART objective
D. Program objective

152. _____ bias represents a threat to internal validity of findings because the participants in the treatment differed from those in the control group.

A. Selection
B. Seasonal
C. Mortality
D. Maturation effect

153. When using presentation software, it is considered a best practice to do:

A. Use a lot of animations to keep the audience interested
B. Practice the presentation before presenting it in public
C. Limit the text on the slides to only the most important concepts
D. B and C

154. A health educator is interested in understanding what health services are needed by employees in a certain company. Which of the following audiences would be least helpful to consult?

    A. Employees
    B. Management
    C. Former employees
    D. Human resources department

155. Descriptive study designs include which of the following except?

    A. Cross-sectional
    B. Case-control
    C. Cohort
    D. Pretest-posttest design

156. A health educator has been asked to write a literature review about using gene therapy in spinal cord injury patients. Which would be the least appropriate database to search for studies?

    A. PsycInfo
    B. CINAHL
    C. Medline
    D. EBMR

157. Which of the following social networking sites are adults in the United States most likely to use?

    A. Facebook
    B. Twitter
    C. Instagram
    D. MySpace

158. A health education specialist working in an OB/GYN clinic in an under-resourced area has been tasked with developing a brochure for expectant mothers explaining to them the importance of being screened for several infectious diseases during pregnancy. Many of the mothers did not graduate high school. The best approach for developing such a brochure would be to:

    A. Download a brochure from the state health department for expectant mothers on screening in pregnancy.
    B. Create a brochure based on the health educator's experience with the topic.
    C. Draft a brochure and then get feedback from patients at the clinic.
    D. Draft a brochure and ask a doctor at the clinic to review it.

159. Which of the following are the least likely for a health educator to be able to influence in a community?

    A. Biological factors such as genetics
    B. Psychosocial factors such as public acceptance for people with disabilities
    C. Environmental factors such as lead in drinking water
    D. Behavioral factors such as increasing vegetable consumption

160. Low health literacy is associated with which outcomes?

    A. Better communication with clinicians
    B. Overuse of emergency room services
    C. Lower risk of adverse outcomes
    D. Increased medication compliance

161. A health educator is asked to address the topic of obesity in a senior care center. Many of the seniors receive food stamps and have limited health literacy skills. The health educator believes that it is critical to use a variety of methods to help address the problem. Which of the following are essential to the health educator's programs' success?

    A. An e-learning facility
    B. Adequate funding
    C. Dance classes
    D. A and B

162. By far, the greatest number of Americans speak English or Spanish. What are the three next most commonly spoken languages, in order of their frequency of use?

    A. Chinese, Tagalog, Vietnamese
    B. French, Chinese, Vietnamese
    C. Arabic, Vietnamese, French
    D. Tagalog, French, Arabic

163. Which of the following would be an inappropriate technology to distribute information on diabetes to a deaf population?

    A. Podcast
    B. Website
    C. Television segment
    D. Text-messaging

164. Where is the error in this logic model (Figure 9.3)?

    A. The inputs are actually outputs
    B. The activities are not achievable
    C. The short-term outcomes are not theory-based
    D. The medium and long-term outcomes are not plausible

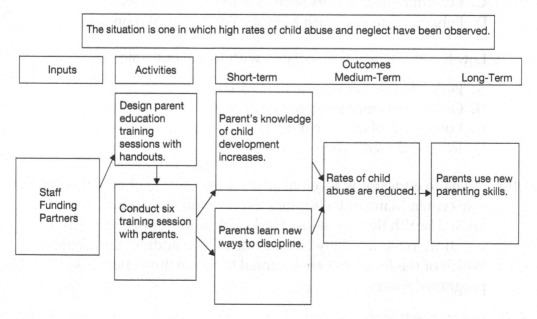

Figure 9.3. Logic Model for a situation in which high rates of child abuse and neglect have been observed.

165. When searching for health information online, the most important issue for a health educator to consider for each website is:

    A. Whether the site has attractive colors and pictures
    B. If the website has a search feature
    C. If all sources are cited using the American Psychological Association (APA) style
    D. The relevance of the information to the intended audience

When you check your answers, is there one or more Areas of Responsibility you feel you need to review? Remember, we strongly encourage you to use other materials in addition to this guide to help you review!

ANSWERS

1. A. Primary (Area VI)

Primary sources are those containing original research or data. Secondary sources such as newspaper or magazine articles synthesize or report on primary source material

2. B. Secondary (Area VI)

3. C. Analyzing focus group data (Area III)

In preparation for implementation, you might hire and train staff, issue RFPs and award funds, or produce written or online materials. Analyses of focus group materials, while potentially helpful for developing or evaluating programs, is the least like the other operational activities.

4. D. Change underlying assumptions (Area IV)

A logic model can and should identify underlying assumptions, but it cannot change them.

5. D. Considers enabling factors (Area II)

Phase 1 of PRECEED–PROCEED is the Social Diagnosis Phase. Enabling factors are considered in Phase 3.

6. B. Positively skewed (Area IV)

Negative skewed graphs have tails to the left. Positive skewed graphs have tails to the right.

7. D. A and C (Area V)

Program proposals often contain specific aims, which set the scope of the project, and include letters of support from organizations that will be involved with the program.

8. C. Will the technology be acceptable to or wanted by the population? (Area V)

The first question must be if the population is, "Does the population want this technology?" "Is it acceptable to them?" Only after those questions are answered can other questions be asked.

9. D. Equity (Area V)

By not only considering whether physical disabilities will prevent use, but by actually using technology to overcome physical limitations, as well as ensuring that financial resources are not a barrier, the ethical principle of equity is being upheld.

10. C. Use technical jargon (Area IV)

Knowing your audience and the requirements for reporting is always key, but when writing evaluation reports, it is best to avoid technical jargon and use clear, straightforward language to communicate the salient points. Illustrations, examples, and stories make for engaging reading.

11. B. Knowledge (Area VI)

Knowledge (or Remembering) is the lowest level in Bloom's Taxonomy.

12. D. Budget justification (Area V)

Budget justifications describe proposed costs for a project. Generally, they explain staffing and supply costs in sufficient detail for a reviewer to understand the necessity for each proposed cost within the project.

13. C. Tailoring (Area III)

Tailored messages are custom fitted to an individual, or groups of individuals, based upon particular characteristics they hold. These frequently include stage-of-change, demographic factors, or health condition or behavior.

14. B. Institutional Review Board (Area III)

Institutional Review Boards (IRB) can also be known as Independent Ethics Committees (IEC) or Ethical Review Boards (ERB) in the United States.

15. C. Enabling (Area II)

Enabling factors are those factors in the environment that facilitate action and any skills or resources that are required to perform specific behavior. These can include resources such as funding.

16. C. Focus on improving knowledge rather than changing behavior (Area VI)

Using headings and subheads, avoiding or at least defining jargon, and using white space are all best practices for creating readable materials. Increasing knowledge, rather than changing behavior, might or might not be an appropriate goal in a specific instance, but is not necessarily a best practice.

17. C. Logic model (Area IV)

Logic models are a graphical depiction of the logical relationships between the resources (inputs), activities, outputs, and outcomes of a program.

18. A. Implementation, process evaluation, impact evaluation, outcome evaluation (Area II)

The four phases of the PROCEED Model are implementation, process evaluation, impact evaluation, outcome evaluation.

19. B. Confidentiality (Area III)

Article 1, Section 6 of the *Code of Ethics for the Health Education Profession* states that "Health Educators are ethically bound to respect, assure, and protect the privacy, confidentiality, and dignity of individuals."

20. B. Is not intended to be generalizable to a wider population (Area IV)

Program evaluation is intended to judge the merit or worth of a particular program, not to produce generalizable knowledge.

21. A. First (Area I)

In 2010, heart disease killed 597,689 Americans, making it the number one cause of death (CDC; www.cdc.gov/mmwr/preview/mmwrhtml/mm6208a8.htm).

22. D. Immunization (Area II)

Primary preventions, like immunizations, seek to prevent disease. Secondary preventions seek to detect diseases early so they can be treated before they become more serious.

23. A. Coercive (Area III)

A very high value incentive ($500) could be considered coercive because people could be persuaded into taking the vaccination simply to receive the incentive. This is particularly true given that the intervention is taking place in a low-income area.

24. D. Ethical (Area III)

Coercive incentives are a violation of Article IV, Section 5 of the *Code of Ethics for The Health Education Profession*.

25. A. Inferential (Area IV)

Inferential statistics makes inferences about a population based on a sample of data taken from the population.

26. B. Left-to- right or right-to-left (Area IV)

When constructing a logic model from the left, the resources available lead to activities, and the activities to the outcomes (sometimes referred to as "if . . . then" construction). When constructing logic models right-to-left, the desired outcomes drive the necessary activities, and the activities necessitate the resources (commonly referred to as the "but how?" construction).

27. B. Secondary prevention (Area II)

Secondary prevention, such as mammography, uses screening techniques to identify disease early to reduce morbidity and mortality.

28. D. A and C (Area V)

Asking new hires about their health status, even in seemingly innocuous ways, could be illegal.

29. A. Advocacy strategies (Area VII)

Advocacy techniques can include encouraging potential voters to register and electioneering, or actively taking part in the activities of a particular candidate's campaign.

30. D. Informed consent (Area III)

Informed consent is the means by which researchers provide information to potential participants on the potential risks and benefits of being involved in a research study. The specifics of informed consent will be dictated by an Institutional Review Board (IRB), but would include the duration, risks and benefits, and requirements of the study.

31. C. Fidelity monitoring (Area IV)

Fidelity monitoring ensures that the program is implemented as it was intended.

32. D. The conference attendee will be able to demonstrate how to perform cardiopulmonary resuscitation (CPR). (Area II)

Learning objectives should be student-centered, use action verbs (ideally from Bloom's Taxonomy, and should break down the task a focus on specific, measurable cognitive, or skill-based processes.

33. C. Justice (Area III)

The Belmont Report, published in 1979, calls for beneficence, respect for persons, and justice.

34. A. The smoking rate for male children and adults aged 18 to 44 was essentially the same. (Area I)

Looking at Figure 9.2, in 2001, the rates of smoking for males in grades 9 through 12 and males aged 18 to 44 are nearly the same, making this the best answer.

35. B. A brief uptick in smoking rates in males, followed by a return to baseline (Area I)

The figure shows that males had a brief increase in smoking in 2006, which returned to around 10% for the remaining years. Female seniors' rates remained under 10% for the period.

36. C. Women over the age of 65 (Area I)

Female seniors' rates remained between under 10% for the period.

37. A. Engaging stakeholders (Area IV)

The steps in the CDC Evaluation Framework are: (a) engage stakeholders, (b) describe program, (c) focus evaluation design, (d) gather credible evidence, (e) justify conclusions, (f) use and share lessons learned. www.cdc.gov/eval/framework/index.htm

38. A. Quality assurance (Area III)

Merriam-Webster defines "quality assurance" as "a program for the systematic monitoring and evaluation of the various aspects of a project, service, or facility to ensure that standards of quality are being met."

39. A. Assess needs, write goals/objectives, choose channel(s), implement, evaluate (Area VII)

First you must define the problem, set goals/objectives, develop your intervention (including choosing your channels), implement your plan, and then evaluate to see how it went. See www.cdc.gov/healthcommunication/healthbasics/HowToDo.html for more information.

40. C. Reading level (Area VII)

These are all tools you use when assessing reading level for health literacy work.

41. D. Behavioral objective (Area II)

The main difference between goals and objectives is their specificity. Goals are more general and include words such as "increase, decrease, raise, lower" but without specifics. Here, the targets and timeframe identify this as an objective. The objective is targeting a behavior, rather than a knowledge, makes it a behavioral objective, rather than a learning objective.

42. A. Reliability/validity (Area IV)

Reliability refers to the repeatability of findings. If the study were to be done a second, third, or fourth time, would it yield the same results? If so, the data are reliable. Validity refers to the credibility of the research.

43. D. Summative (Area IV)

Summative, or outcome evaluation, seeks to understand whether there was a change in the population in some manner—often in their health status.

44. D. Health Belief Model (Area III)

People can be influenced by the perceived severity, susceptibility, benefits (or threats) of a particular behavior or health condition, according to the Health Belief Model.

45. B. Teach Back (Area VI)

Utilizing the Teach Back Method can be very effective for making sure your audience understood what they were being taught. This technique may be especially useful when teaching those with low levels of health literacy who cannot rely on written instructions. www.ahrq.gov/professionals/quality-patient-safety/quality-resources/tools/literacy-toolkit/healthlittoolkit2-tool5.html

46. C. Educational (Area VII)

Educational media is designed to supplement instruction by highlighting main points and aiding the audience in retaining information.

47. D. Young women of color (Area VII)

The primary audience is nearly always the best source of information for the development and design of messages. Secondary audiences, such as teachers, nurses, and pediatricians, might be valuable sources of information, but the young women would be the true experts on what would be the best social media messages to write.

48. B. Health literacy (Area VI)

Health literacy is dependent on individual and systemic factors including: communication skills of lay persons and professionals, lay and professional knowledge of health topics, culture, demands of the healthcare and public health systems, and the demands of the situation/context.

49. A. Patrons purchase more fresh fruits and vegetables (Area VI)

Determining the best days to sell produce would be an example of a formative evaluation outcome. The vendor tracking the number of produce items offered is a process outcome. Rates of diabetes would be an example of a long-term outcome. Produce consumption, which could influence diabetes rates, is a medium-term outcome.

50. C. Action (Area III)

The Action stage of the Transtheoretical Model encompasses people who have recently changed their behavior and intend to continue to exhibit the changed behavior.

51. A. Healthfinder.gov (Area VI)

Healthfinder.gov is a public-facing website with health promotion information. The others are databases designed for academic or professional use.

52. B. Continuous throughout the program (Area IV)

Program monitoring should be on-going throughout the implementation of a program. It is the method by which evaluations ensure that program activities are being implemented according to the program plan and that problems are addressed in a timely, ethical, and systematic way. It is not optional, and may be contain qualitative, quantitative, or mixed methods.

53. C. Observational learning (Area III)

By offering credible role models who display the targeted behavior, you are demonstrating observational learning or modeling, which is a construct in the Social Cognitive Theory.

54. D. Vision statement (Area II)

Vision statements tend to be more aspirational and forward looking while mission statements are more concrete and focus on what the organization currently does. Vision can be thought of as "where we are going" and mission is "how we are going to get there."

55. C. Inputs (Area III)

In a logic model, inputs are the resources you need to conduct a program.

56. D. Outputs (Area III)

In a logic model, outputs are the activities or products produced by the program. In this case, classes, or a website would be activities or products created by a program, thus outputs.

57. B. They should be determined at the beginning of the planning process (Area II)

Program goals and objectives should be determined at the beginning of the planning process to guide the development of the plan. Without goals and objectives, a health educator would not have anything to guide the development of the project.

58. D. EBMR (Area IV)

EBMR (Evidence-Based Medicine Reviews) is a database of evidence-based medical interventions.

59. B. Direct cost (Area V)

Direct cost is the part of the budget which contributes directly to the program's outputs.

60. B. Secondary (Area II)

Secondary audiences are those who can help reach or influence the intended or primary audience (in this case, the men in need of primary care).

61. A. In-person interviews (Area I)

In-person interviews are very costly to conduct because they are very labor intensive.

62. D. Attitude (Area III)

In the Theory of Planned Behavior, the construct of "attitude" refers to the degree to which a person has a favorable or unfavorable evaluation of the behavior of interest including a consideration of the outcomes of performing the behavior. Since the woman strongly believes she will gain weight if she quits smoking, this represents an attitude toward quitting smoking.

63. A. Using and sharing results (Area IV)

The sixth and final step is "Use and Share Lessons Learned."

64. A. Health education (Area I)

Health problems that are highly changeable and highly important to the population are likely to be able to be influenced through an educational approach.

65. C. Establish a program management system (Area III)

Gantt charts are often used to ensure that programs are operating on schedule and that activities occur in the order they need to.

66. B. Comprehensiveness (Area VII)

Social marketing has clearly defined behavioral goals and focuses on those goals specifically. Programs do need to cost-effective, thoroughly informed by market research, and always recognize competition.

67. A. Face-to-face meetings (Area III)

Studies have shown that, of the above choices, personal contact best facilitated use of information by policy makers.

68. B. Sense of mission (Area VI)

Understanding the mission, vision, values, beliefs, and ethics of an organization is to exhibit a sense of the mission of an organization. It does not necessarily imply that one has leadership skills, or political competencies, but can articulate the core principles and philosophies of the organization.

69. A. CINAHL (Area V)

CINAHL is the database for nursing and allied health professionals.

70. D. A and B (Area IV)

A data analysis and reporting plan would never a priori presume any findings.

71. A. Education (Area III)

In a novel situation where most people are simply unaware of a risk and there are few barriers to performing a behavior (in this case, not playing a game while driving) education is likely the easiest, least expensive, and thus the first choice of intervention.

72. D. Legislation (Area III)

When education and persuasive techniques have failed to bring about the desired levels of behavior change, legal solutions are often employed.

73. C. Who is our competition? (Area V)

Strategic plans focus on the organization, and things in the organization's control—where it is, where it wants to go, and how it is going to get there.

74. B. Prioritize strategies for the next 5 years (Area VI)

Strategic plans usually prioritize strategies for organizations to employ over the next 5 years.

75. C. SWOT (Area VI)

A SWOT (Strengths, Weaknesses, Opportunities, Threats) analysis helps planners understand the situation in which their program will be operating.

76. D. Outcome (Area IV)

Outcome or effectiveness *evaluation* measures program effects in the target population by assessing the progress toward the *outcome* objectives of the program, whether there were unintended effects, how acceptable the program was, and so on.

77. B. Measurable (Area II)

Objectives must be measurable to quantify or measure progress.

78. C. Product, price, place, and promotion (Area VII)

The *product* (tangible or intangible) satisfies the consumer's needs or wants, the *price* is what the customer pays (in direct or indirect costs), the *place* is where the customer accesses the product, and the *promotion* is the marketing communication.

79. C. Innovators (Area III)

Innovators are the very first to adopt a behavior. Early adopters are next.

80. A. Talk to students about their health concerns (Area I)

Assessing needs with the target population is an important first step in program planning.

81. A. Consulting (Area VI)

82. C. Health Belief Model (Area III)

"Perceived susceptibility" is another way of saying "perceived threat of a disease," a core construct of the Health Belief Model.

83. B. Outside your control (Area II)

Strengths and weaknesses are within the origination's control. Opportunities and threats are outside the organization's control.

84. B. Strengths (Area II)

The strengths of an intervention are the internal, positive factors of the intervention, that is, the parts of the intervention that are controllable by the project design and are considered to be those that will help to achieve the project's goals and objectives (i.e., what the program planners think will make the program work).

85. D. Determine the objectives of the focus group> Determine the focus group questions to be asked> Determine a data analysis plan> Recruit participants (Area I)

Qualitative data are collected methodically, just as quantitative data are. First the objectives of the study are determined. Then questions would be created to capture the data needed to satisfy project objectives. Next a data analysis plan would be constructed to ensure that the data could be obtained from the questions asked, and the methods for doing so (number of coders, method of coding, etc.). Only after that would recruitment of participations begin.

86. C. Geographical limitations (Area I)

Conducting surveys remotely can eliminate or reduce geographical limitations to research.

87. D. Even if you design, recruit, and analyze your focus groups well, you may need additional needs assessment information (Area I)

Focus groups can provide rich and deep information, but they should not be considered the sole source of information because they are not representative. Individual focus groups generally should be homogenous to facilitate honest opinion sharing—in this case, mixing management and labor might constrain employees' willingness to share their opinions.

88. B. Nominal (Area IV)

Nominal data can also be thought of as "named" data ("red, blue, green" or "high, medium, low").

89. B. MOU (Area V)

A Memorandum of Understanding (MOU) is a more informal document than a Memorandum of Agreement (MOA), which can have legal implications.

90. D. Exposure to toxic substances (Area III)

Exposure to toxic substance is a biological factor, though may be influenced by things like poverty, poor housing, and so on, which would be addressed in the Social Ecological Model.

91. B. Teaching strategies (Area VI)

Varying teaching strategies can make sure you are addressing the needs of different types of learners.

92. C. Change in knowledge (Area VI)

Pretest-posttest evaluation is best suited to test a change in something, such as knowledge, attitude, or skill.

93. A. Assessing existing health needs and problems (Area II)

Planning begins with assessing the situation and identifying the health problems that are occurring.

94. A. Process evaluation (Area IV)

Process evaluation monitors to make sure things are being implemented as planned and to ensure that mid-course corrections are not needed. If, when cooking, you have ever tasted a recipe to make sure it tastes good as you were cooking it, you have conducted process evaluation!

95. B. Change of attitude, acquisition of skills, short-term retention of information, long-term retention of information, decision making, reinforcement of behavior, maintenance of behavior (Area III)

The Hierarchy of Effects model describes the process people go through as they decide to buy goods or adopt behaviors.

96. A. Experimental (Area III)

Experimental (or Treatment) studies come in a variety of randomized controlled trials and quasi-experimental forms

97. C. Needs assessment data (Area II)

Ideally, the needs assessment should drive the development of the goals and objectives for the program. BRFSS (Behavioral Risk Factor Surveillance System) data are a valuable source of population-level data but cannot provide specifics about conditions faced by the local nonprofit or their clients or partners. Finally, while other's evaluation data can be useful to help inform your project, it should not dominate your thinking.

98. C. Valid (Area I)

Valid measures measure what they are supposed to—if you get on a scale, it will tell you what you actually weigh. Reliable measures will work each time.

99. D. Correlation (Area IV)

Correlation cannot imply causation.

100. C. Mixed methods (Area I)

A mixed methods approach can provide program planners with a balance between the efficiency and generalizability of quantitative methods like surveys while balancing out their limitations of lack of context and shallowness of the data by supplementing them with qualitative methods such as interviews and focus groups to gain richer, deeper understanding of participant needs and perspectives. These relatively more expensive and less generalizable methods can be used where needed as either exploration to inform the development of the quantitative work, or to further explore themes found in the quantitative needs assessment that program planners do not understand and need more information about to move forward.

101. D. Capricious (Area VII)

Health communication materials should always be clear, credible, and consistent. Capriciousness, or being given to sudden and unaccountable changes of mood or behavior, is not a desirable quality in health communication materials.

102. A. The costs of training volunteers to transport participants in such a way to satisfy liability concerns (Area V)

Using volunteers to transport participants might incur significant costs to receive certifications to satisfy insurance and other legal or regulatory agencies. Training costs can be a significant barrier for implementation of programs.

103. C. Employee leisure-time activities (Area IV)

While employee leisure-time activities do contribute significantly to overall health and well-being, they are outside of the control of an employer and a worksite health promotion program.

104. A. Ecological Model (Area III)

The Ecological Model seeks to explain how many factors from the individual through the interpersonal, societal, and policy interact to influence health.

105. B. In-depth interviews (Area I)

In-depth interviews, participant observations, and focus group data are all examples of qualitative data.

106. C. Innate, intrapersonal, interpersonal, institutional, community, public policy (Area III)

The Social Ecological Model sees health as being influenced by a series of interconnected systems. The innate are those biological factors a person is born with. The intrapersonal are an individual's knowledge, attitudes, behaviors, skills, and so on. Intrapersonal processes and primary groups are the formal and informal social networks and support systems surrounding the individual, such as families, work, and friendship networks. The next larger circle are institutional factors, such as social institutions and organizations, including formal and informal rules and regulations. Next, community factors, including relationships among organizations and institutions and informal networks. Finally, the outermost circle, furthest from the individual on the model are public policy including laws and policies.

107. D. Randomized control study (Area IV)

Randomized Controlled Trials (RCTs) are considered the "gold standard" of causational studies.

108. A. Gain attention (Area VI)

First you have to have people's attention before you can begin to provide instruction. The next step is to "Inform the learners of the objectives."

109. B. Young men who have been convicted of DUI (Area III)

Young men who have been convicted of a DUI are the target audience for the intervention and thus have valuable insight into the causes of the problem and the needs of the audience.

110. D. Interactions (Area III)

The model is predicated on the idea the multiple levels of the model interact with each other.

111. A. Extending personal invitations through staff, stakeholders, or clients (Area V)

Expanding a volunteer network through those already involved with your organization is likely to be the most effective method of recruitment because it leverages existing relationships. Personalized requests are more likely to be responded to than mass requests like those over social or mass media.

112. D. A and C (Area VII)

Headings, bulleted list, and chunking similar information into small, manageable pieces and some of the ways you can create documents that are easier for readers to navigate.

113. B. Primary (Area I)

Primary research is new research which you have carried out to answer a specific question or set of questions.

114. B. Direct, indirect, and in-kind donations (Area II)

Your budget should reflect direct, or those costs related solely to the project's operations, indirect, costs not entirely attributable to the project (e.g., rent, utilities, staff working indirectly on the project like Human Resources), and in-kind donations.

115. C. Tailored (Area III)

Tailored health communications have been shown to be effective in a variety of situations but are more expensive to produce and maintain.

116. D. 12 months (Area II)

A national health communication campaign can easily take a year or better to plan, including developing and testing materials.

117. A. The program's activities and outputs (Area IV)

Process indicators measure the programs outputs—whether program activities have been implemented as intended. Examples include—how many classes were held, how many posters were displayed, social media ads were run?

118. B. Jargon or technical language (Area VII)

The audience for a press release are the members of the print, television, and (to some extent) the online media. Therefore, they are written in professional, but neutral language, free from jargon or technical terms.

119. D. ERIC (Area VI)

ERIC (Education Resources Information Center) is an online library of education research and information, sponsored by the Institute of Education Sciences (IES) of the U.S. Department of Education.

120. A. Conduct a community analysis (Area I)

Begin with an analysis of the situation facing the community to determine what needs the community faces. You cannot understand reinforcing factors until you have determined a particular health problem. You do not know which segment of the population's health literacy to investigate until you have determined which subsegments to address. And you cannot write a budget until much later in the planning process.

121. D. A and C (Area V)

While using volunteers will save on paying salaries, it still takes time and money to recruit and train them, and it is important to provide rewards, both extrinsic and intrinsic, to both volunteers and staff, to keep them engaged and satisfied with their work, though obviously the nature of those rewards vary depending on their relationship with the organization.

122. B. Make sure everyone in the group speaks (Area VII)

Usually it is best to identify one or two people to speak on behalf of the group. Meetings with legislators are usually short and limiting the number of people who speak keeps the meeting on track and keeps your message consistent.

123. C. Interviews (Area VI)

Interviews are usually examples of primary data.

124. D. Cohort (Area III)

A **cohort study** is a longitudinal study selected from a cohort, (sharing a defining characteristic, such as birth or graduation), performing a cross-sectional studies at intervals through time.

125. C. 40% (Area VII)

Studies show that 40% of Americans have inadequate levels of health literacy, and only 12% are in the "proficient" category.

126. D. Observations (Area I)

Observations provide direct information about behavior of individuals and groups, permit evaluators to enter into and understand situation and/or context and provide opportunities for identifying unanticipated outcomes, all hallmarks of qualitative data.

127. D. Describe how they will measure variables in program (Area II)

The methods section is the place to describe how variables will be measured in the project.

128. A. Emphasize the instructor's education and experience (Area VI)

When an audience is reluctant, making the information relevant to them is especially important. Stress what value the new information brings to their lives—does it make their job easier to perform? Does it make their children healthier? What does it get them that they want?

129. B. Find out more about the audience (Area VI)

Understanding the audience to whom he will be presenting will be critical. Some questions he might want to ask are: How many people will be there? Were they involved in the assessment? Are they receptive or hostile to the findings? How long will they be planning on staying? Have they been to a meeting like this before? What are they expecting him to say? What questions do they have? What style of presentation should he use? Should he use PowerPoint?

130. A. Learning objective (Area III)

Learning objectives are important because they give students a sense of what to expect in a course and guide the instructor's assessment strategies.

131. C. Pilot project (Area III)

A pilot is a trial of an intervention in its entirety run in a limited location. The results are used to fix problems and make changes before a full-scale project implementation.

132. B. Grassroots advocacy/direct advocacy (Area VII)

Grassroots advocacy harnesses the power of the public to bring pressure upon elected officials to make policy changes, as opposed to direct advocacy, or lobbying, which relies on paid or volunteer staff to lobby officials for change.

133. C. Justify (Area VI)

"List" comes from the "Remembering" or lowest domain. "Use" comes from the "Applying" or third domain. Analyze comes from the "Analyzing" or fourth domain. "Justify" comes from the "Evaluating" or fifth domain.

134. B. A model can draw on a series of theories to help describe a problem in a specific context. (Area II)

A model provides the individual with a structural representation of the phenomenon, allowing her or him to gain a fuller understanding of it. On the other hand, a theory is a set of ideas that provide an explanation to something.

135. B. Process, outcome, impact (Area IV)

Most program evaluation will investigate process, outcome, and impact evaluation, though some will be limited to one, or two of the above (i.e., merely a process evaluation)

136. D. Done it and taught it to someone else (Area II)

The old adage from medical school is when you are learning something you "see one, do one, teach one." Practicing a skill and teaching it to someone else under supervised conditions is a most effective way of learning information.

137. C. Sharing and validating the needs that have been identified (Area I)

Validating the results of your needs assessment with the community will confirm that the priorities the needs assessment has identified are appropriate and acceptable to the community.

138. A. Strategic planning (Area V)

The strategic planning process usually happens in a 5-year cycle and involves thinking holistically about all aspects of the organization's outputs and activities.

139. D. Is the information written in an active or passive voice? (Area VI)

While active voice is preferred for readability, it is not important for assessing the quality of online information. In this case, questions like the source of the information, are sources and citations offered, and is there a date that the site was last updated are more imported for assessing the quality of the website.

140. B. The use of structured questionnaires used to generate consensus in a group of experts (Area I)

A Delphi method is a small-group research technique that seeks a consensus among experts through sequential rounds of data collection and reduction.

141. B. TV (Area III)

Because of its ubiquity and that TV is an audiovisual news source, it is the choice for people with low literacy levels.

142. A. Pilot test (Area III)

A pilot test would test just the materials for a project. The pilot project would test the entire implementation in a small geographical area.

143. A. 18 to 29 (Area VI)

Younger people are more likely than older people to use the Internet, according to the Pew Internet and American Life Study. Ninety-nine percent of those 18 to 29 use the Internet, 96% of those 30 to 49, 87% of those 50 to 64, and 64% of those 65+.

144. C. Launch a pilot project in one neighborhood (Area II)

Holding more focus groups is unlikely to turn up new data—she has reached saturation on this point. It is also unlikely she has reached the point in a program where she has held several focus groups and developed a program to this extent without having conducted a literature search on safe sleep. And given that the community has clearly expressed a need and desire, focusing on something else is not an acceptable choice. She is ready to launch a pilot project and see what opportunities and challenges exist implementing the project.

145. C. What will solve the problem? (Area I)

The Epidemiological Model for needs assessment focuses on identifying problems, not identifying solutions.

146. D. CINAHL (Area I)

CINAHL is the database for nursing and allied health professionals. The rest are common sources of secondary data.

147. B. If students will be embarrassed by the curriculum (Area II)

In considering a school-based curriculum, a school board would want to investigate cost, parental support (because parents could be a substantial roadblock to a sexual-health curriculum being implemented in schools) and gather feedback about other user's experiences of other existing curricula. While the student experience is important, some embarrassment in discussing this topic in school is less concerning than the curriculum being evidence-based, acceptable to the community at large, affordable, and implemented appropriately.

148. B. Avoid repetition (Area II)

Rather than avoiding repetition, the instructor should repeat key information, in interesting ways, throughout the instruction. Most people need to encounter new information more than once and in a variety of ways before they fully take in new information, especially if it is complex or particularly unfamiliar. Put another way, "practice makes perfect."

149. D. Cross-sectional (Area III)

Cross-sectional studies are onetime studies that give researchers a "snapshot" of what is going on at a particular point in time. They are useful for determining prevalence of a health problem among other things.

150. A. A teachable moment (Area II)

Teachable moments are periods in time when events lend themselves to provide illustrations of concepts taught in educational materials. They can also be opportunities (from a SWOT analysis) or external, positive events for a campaign—moments that support the objectives of your campaign within the context of your community or give rise to the need for your campaign.

151. A. Behavioral objective (Area III)

Behavioral objectives give the learner a sense of what specifically they will be able to do after completing the course.

152. A. Selection (Area IV)

The concern with selection bias is that somehow the participants in the treatment and control groups were, from the beginning, somehow different and that any difference between the groups was related to those preexisting differences and not treatment effect. This can happen if the groups are not sufficiently randomized into treatment and control arms.

153. D. B and C (Area VI)

Practicing the presentation beforehand ensures that you are comfortable delivering the presentation and that your talk can be delivered in the appropriate amount of time. Limiting the text on the slide to only the key concepts helps make sure that it is readable to as wide of an audience as possible and that the key concepts are remembered by the audience. A lot of animations can be distracting and may not be appropriate depending on the topic and audience.

154. C. Former employees (Area I)

While former employees might have some valuable insights, it is current employees that are the audience of a worksite health promotion program. Given an unlimited budget and time-frame, it might be worth speaking to former employees to see if they had left the company due to a lack of health services, but from a realistic standpoint, it make much more sense to focus resources on speaking to current employees, management, and those in the human resources (HR) Department.

155. D. Pretest-posttest design (Area III)

Cross-sectional, cohort, case-control all help researchers describe or observe what is going on in various populations, but the researchers do not try to change what is being experienced by those populations in the course of conducting the research. In experimental designs, such as randomized controlled trials (RCTs) or a pretest-posttest quasi-experimental design, researchers are trying to effect change in the study population.

156. A. PsycINFO (Area VI)

PsychINFO is a resource for abstracts and journal articles on behavioral and social science research. The other three databases of medical journals, and therefore better choices for the topic of gene therapy.

157. A. Facebook (Area VI)

According to the Pew Internet and American Life Survey, in 2016, approximately 68% of Americans use Facebook.

158. C. Draft a brochure and then get feedback from patients at the clinic (Area III)

Because the mothers at the clinic have special characteristics (i.e., many did not graduate from high school, which makes the different from the general population), it would be best to create and test materials with this population to ensure the materials are a good fit for their needs. The patients at the clinic are the true experts as to their needs and desires for materials.

159. A. Biological factors such as genetics (Area I)

Biological factors are the least able to be influenced by health education. Health education is much more able to influence psychosocial and behavioral factors, and can influence people's responses to, and mitigation of environmental factors.

160. B. Overuse of emergency room services (Area VI)

Patients with low health literacy are more likely to use the emergency room, have medication errors, and cost the healthcare system billions of dollars in excess funds each year.

161. B. Adequate funding (Area III)

In this case, the instructor simply needs adequate funding. With adequate funding, he or she can develop a program that fits the needs of the seniors. It is premature at this stage of program development to speculate whether dance classes or an e-learning facility (or any other particular intervention) will be appropriate.

162. A. Chinese, Tagalog, Vietnamese (Area VII)

According to the U.S. Census Bureau, 2011 the five most frequently spoken languages in the United States are (a) English, (b) Spanish, (c) Chinese, (d) Tagalog, and (e) Vietnamese.

163. A. Podcast (Area III)

Podcasts are an entirely audio-based medium, and thus inappropriate for a deaf audience. There have been some limited efforts to transcribe some podcasts for a deaf or hard-of-hearing audience, but a different channel should be selected at this time.

164. D. The medium and long-term outcomes are not plausible
    (Area IV)

In this case, the long-term objective "parents use new parenting skills" is a behavioral objective that the reduction in morbidity "rates of child abuse are reduced" is predicated upon. Thus, the logical flow of the model is backwards.

165. D. The relevance of the information to the intended audience
    (Area VI)

When evaluating websites, accuracy, relevance, and appropriateness to the intended audience are among the most important features to look for. Others include a clear understanding of who the author is and when the last time the site was updated.

Evaluation of Results					
Area of Responsibility	Question Numbers	Number of Questions	Number Correct	Percentage Correct	Topics Requiring Further Study?
1. Area I: Assess Needs, Assets, and Capacity for Health Education	21, 34, 35, 36, 61, 64, 80, 85, 86, 87, 98, 100, 105, 113, 120, 126, 137, 140, 145, 146, 154, 159	22	__/22	%	
2. Area II: Plan Health Education/ Promotion	5, 15, 18, 22, 27, 32, 41, 54, 57, 60, 77, 83, 84, 93, 97, 114, 116, 127, 134, 136, 144, 147, 148, 150	24	__/24	%	
3. Area III: Implement Health Education/ Promotion	3, 13, 14, 19, 23, 24, 30, 33, 38, 44, 50, 53, 55, 56, 62, 65, 67, 71, 72, 79, 82, 90, 95, 96, 104, 106, 109, 110, 115, 124, 130, 131, 141, 142, 149, 151, 155, 158, 161, 163	40	__/40	%	

(Continued)

Evaluation of Results					
Area of Responsibility	**Question Numbers**	**Number of Questions**	**Number Correct**	**Percentage Correct**	**Topics Requiring Further Study?**
4. Area IV: Conduct Evaluation and Research Related to Health Education/ Promotion	4, 6, 10, 17, 20 25, 26, 31, 37, 42, 43, 52, 58, 63, 70, 76, 88, 94, 99, 103, 107, 117, 135, 152, 164	25	__/25	%	
5. Area V: Administer and Manage Health Education/ Promotion	7, 8, 9, 12, 28, 59, 69, 73, 89, 102, 111, 121, 138	13	__/13	%	
6. Area VI: Serve As a Health Education/ Promotion Resource Person	1, 2, 11, 16, 45, 48, 49, 51, 68, 74, 75, 81, 91, 92, 108, 119, 123, 128, 129, 133, 139, 143, 153, 156, 157, 160, 165	27	__/27	%	
7. Area VII: Communicate, Promote, and Advocate for Health, Health Education/ Promotion, and the Profession	29, 39, 40, 46, 47, 66, 78, 101, 112, 118, 122, 125, 132, 162	14	__/14	%	

Chapter 10

So Now You Are a
CHES®: What Is Next?

CAREER OPPORTUNITIES FOR HEALTH EDUCATORS

Congratulations! Once you have passed the Certified Health Education Specialist (CHES®) exam, you will probably be looking for a job in which to use your health education skills. Fortunately, health educators are in demand in a variety of work settings. But where and how should you look for a job as a health educator?

WHAT HEALTH EDUCATORS DO

Health educators teach people about behaviors that prevent illness or injury and promote wellness. They develop and implement strategies to improve the health of individuals and communities.

Health educators typically do the following:

- Provide needs assessment in organizations and communities.
- Develop programs to educate people about health topics or train them in skills needed to maintain health.
- Teach people how to manage health conditions.
- Evaluate the effectiveness of programs and educational materials.

- Help people find health services or information.
- Provide training programs for other health professionals.
- Supervise staff who implement health education programs.
- Collect and analyze data to learn about their audience and improve programs and services.
- Advocate for improved health resources and policies that promote health.

The duties of health educators depend on the work setting. You most likely will work in healthcare facilities, colleges, public health departments, nonprofits, and private businesses. Some CHES® work in secondary school settings as teachers. What follows are some of the most common settings in which CHES® may work, a description of the type of work they might do there, and resources for looking for employment in each setting.

Healthcare Setting

In healthcare facilities, health educators may work one-on-one with patients and their families, or work with other healthcare professionals to improve the care patients receive. They teach patients about their diagnoses and about any necessary treatments or procedures. CHES® may work as patient navigators, helping consumers determine their health insurance options and directing people to outside resources, such as support groups and home health agencies. Health educators in healthcare facilities also help organize health fairs and classes. Professionally, CHES® can collaborate with other health professionals to ensure that health education classes and materials are understandable, culturally appropriate, and easily accessed by patients. Health educators may also be coaches and help patients lose weight, manage chronic disease, or quit smoking.

According to the Bureau of Labor Statistics (BLS), health educator jobs in hospital (government, state, local) settings are the highest paid, with a median salary of $63,510. Salaries for health educators who work in individual and family services are about one third lower, with a median salary of $40,360. In May 2016, about a quarter of all health educators (23%) worked in hospital settings, making it the largest sector that employs health educators.

College Setting

In colleges, health educators create programs and materials on topics that affect young adults, such as sexual health, substance abuse, stress, and sleep. They employ a variety of methods and channels, including health fairs, dining hall nutrition trainings, and social media to make sure students are getting necessary health information. Health educators also advocate for campus policies to promote health, train resident assistants and peer health educators, and liaison with faculty and staff.

Federal, State, or Local Public Health Department Setting

In public health departments, health educators administer public health campaigns on topics such as emergency preparedness, immunizations, proper nutrition, and stress management. They develop materials to be used by other public health officials. During emergencies, they may provide safety information to the public and the media. Some health educators work with other professionals to create public policies that support healthy behaviors and environments. They may also oversee grants and grant-funded programs to improve the health of the public. Some participate in statewide and local committees dealing with topics such as aging.

According to BLS, 22% of health educators were employed in a government setting. As of May 2017, salaries averaged $55,420, though there was a considerable range. Jobs at the local level may pay less than those at the state or national level.

Nonprofit or Community-Based Organization Setting

In nonprofits (including community health organizations), health educators create programs and materials about health issues for the community their organization serves. They help organizations obtain funding and other resources. Many nonprofits focus on a particular disease or audience, so health educators in these organizations limit programs to that specific topic or audience. For example, a health educator may design a program to teach people with diabetes how to better manage their condition, or a program for teen mothers on how to care for their newborns. In addition, health educators may educate policymakers about ways to improve public health and work on securing grant funding for programs to promote health and disease awareness.

While the BLS categorizes things a bit differently, approximately 20% of health education jobs are located in this category. Perhaps not surprisingly, wages are lower in these jobs. According to BLS (May 2017), jobs in the "religious, grantmaking, civic, professional, and similar organizations" category had a median salary of $48,640; those in the "individual and family services" category were the lowest, at a $40,360 median.

Workplace Setting

The workplace is an important setting for health protection, health promotion, and disease prevention programs. On average, Americans who work full-time spend nearly half their waking hours at the workplace.

In private businesses, health educators identify common health problems among employees and create programs to improve health. They work with management to develop incentives for employees to adopt healthy behaviors, such as losing weight or controlling cholesterol. Health educators recommend changes to the workplace, such as creating smoke-free areas, to improve employee health.

Salary Outlook

The median annual wage for health educators was $53,940 in May 2017. An occupation's median wage is the amount at which half its workers earned more and half earned less. In May 2017, the lowest 10% earned less than $31,440; the highest 10% earned more than $97,160.

Hospitals; state, local, and private	$63,510
Government	$55,420
Outpatient health centers	$51,130
Religious, grantmaking, civic, professional, and similar organizations	$48,640
Individual and family services	$40,360

Source: www.bls.gov/ooh/community-and-social-service/health-educators.htm#tab-5

LOOKING FOR A JOB IN HEALTH EDUCATION

There are a number of resources to use when looking for a job in health education. First, your school likely has a career services office that will have resources specific to public health and health education jobs. It can be very fruitful to utilize an alumni contact list, particularly if the alumni's CHES® status is available. Many CHES® find jobs through other CHES®, and it has been our experience that CHES® are happy to help fellow CHES® with job search advice, contacts, and experience.

The following is a list of public health- and health education-specific websites that frequently post the kinds of jobs for which CHES® are qualified:

Public Health Job Search Engines

- American Public Health Association Career Mart (http://careers .apha.org)
- Association of Schools and Programs of Public Health Careers (www.publichealthjobs.net)
- Public Health Employment Connection (https://cfusion.sph .emory.edu/PHEC/phec.cfm)
- Public Health Jobs Worldwide (www.jobspublichealth.com)

Local and State Health Departments

- Association of State and Territorial Health Officials (www.astho .org/Careers-at-ASTHO)
- Maryland Department of Health and Mental Hygiene (www.jobaps .com/md/jobs/dhmh)
- National Association of County and City Health Officials (https:// careers.naccho.org/jobs)
- New York State Department of Health (www.health.ny.gov/ employment)
- Pennsylvania Department of Health (www.health.pa.gov/Your-Department-of-Health/Administrative/Employment/Pages/ default.aspx#.V6yh8fkrLcs)

Academic Opportunities at Schools of Public Health

If you are seeking a research or faculty position at a school of public health, please visit the Association of Schools and Programs of Public Health (ASPPH) website (www.aspph.org) for member schools.

Academic Job Search Engines

- Academic 360 (www.academic360.com)
- Academic Careers Online (http://academiccareers.com)
- Academic Keys for Health Sciences (http://healthsciences .academickeys.com/seeker_job.php)
- AcademyHealth (http://academyhealth.org/career/jobseekers.htm)
- Association of University Programs in Health Administration (www.aupha.org)
- Careers Chronicle of Higher Education (chronicle.com/section/ jobs/61)
- Higher Ed Jobs (www.higheredjobs.com)

Government Opportunities

- Job Search Engine for All Federal Jobs (www.usajobs.gov)
- Centers for Disease Control and Prevention (CDC; www.cdc .gov/employment)
- GovLoop (http://jobs.govloop.com)
- National Institutes of Health (www.jobs.nih.gov)
- U.S. Agency for International Development (USAID; www.usaid .gov/careers)
- U.S. Department of Health and Human Services (www.hhs.gov/ careers)
- Environmental Protection Agency (www.epa.gov/careers)
- U.S. Food and Drug Administration (www.fda.gov/jobs/ default.htm)
- U.S. Public Health Service Commissioned Corps (www.usphs.gov)

International Opportunities

- American Jewish World Service (https://ajws.org/who_we_are/ jobs CARE—www.care.org/careers/index.asp)
- Catholic Relief Services (www.crs.org/about/careers)
- Clinton Health Access Initiative (CHAI; www.fhi360.org/careers)
- Gates Foundation (www.gatesfoundation.org/jobs/pages/ overview.aspx)
- Global Service Corps (www.globalservicecorps.org/site/ how-to-enroll)
- Pan American Health Organization (PAHO; www.paho.org/ english/am/hrm/re/hrm-vacancies.htm)
- PATH(www.path.org/jobs/index.php)
- Peace Corps (www.peacecorps.gov)
- World Health Organization (WHO; www.who.int/employment/ en/index.html)

General Job Search Engines

- Idealist (www.idealist.org)
- Indeed (www.indeed.com)
- Simply Hired (www.simplyhired.com)

MAINTAINING YOUR CERTIFICATION

Passing your test is not the last thing you have to do to be a CHES®. As soon as your certification arrives, you need to start thinking about *maintaining* your credentials. In order to maintain certification, a CHES® must obtain a minimum of 75 Continuing Education Contact Hours (CECH) over the 5-year certification period. National Commission for Health Education Credentialing, Inc. (NCHEC) encourages all CHES® to accumulate a minimum of 15 CECH per year, and to complete all continuing education requirements at least *90 days* prior to recertification.

Within the 75 hours you must accumulate over the 5-year period, there are two types of credits you need.

The first type of credit is Category 1 hours, continuing education hours that have been preapproved by NCHEC. You must have at least 45 of these hours in each 5-year period, though you may earn more. Designated providers—schools, universities, conferences, health departments, and so on—have arrangements with NCHEC and provide it with specific information on their trainings, conferences, and so on . They then request approval for a certain number of Category 1 hours. One of the nice things about Category 1 hours is that they do not require much from you in the way of paperwork—when you attend the event, you provide the registrar with your CHES® number (you might want to save this as a note in your phone so you always have it) and the registrar submits the paperwork to NCHEC for you. Designated providers only have to submit to NCHEC quarterly (which is why NCHEC wants you to have all your hours completed 90 days before recertification is due). Many conferences, meetings, and classes have costs associated with them, but there are sources that offer Category 1 credits for no or very low cost.

Category 2 credits do not require preauthorization and can be claimed by submitting a Category 2 form from NCHEC's website. These credits can include things like attending a meeting for which no Category 1 credits were offered, creating a class or a training, authoring a journal article or a book, or presenting at a conference. Up to 30 Category 2 hours may be claimed in each five-year cycle. If you reside outside of the United States, you may claim all 75 hours as Category 2 credits.

QUESTIONS ABOUT CONTINUING EDUCATION

Yikes! Seventy-five is a lot of hours. How do I manage?

NCHEC recommends that CHES® earn 15 hours a year, and submit their final hours at least 90 days before the end of the recertification cycle. By keeping up each year and spreading the 75 out over the five-year period, it is not terribly burdensome and ensures that you are up-to-date as a practitioner. Think of it as keeping the oil changed in your car—it is just professional maintenance.

How do I know if something is a Category 1 or Category 2 credit?

Usually a training, conference, meeting, or some other approved activity, such as reading a journal article and taking a quiz, will be clearly designated as having Category 1 credits. It will say something like "'X activity' has been pre-approved by NCHEC for 4.0 hours of continuing education," or "4.0 hours have been approved for CHES." If claiming Category 2 credits, be sure to do so within 90 days of having completed the activity.

My job does not pay for continuing education. Where can I find free or low-cost credits?

NCHEC does not charge processing fees to CHES® for continuing education hours, though many of the places that offer CE hours, such as conferences, do charge a fee. However, there are many opportunities for free or low-cost continuing education. The CDC offers many CHES® credits for free at www2a.cdc.gov/tceonline (you will have to create a log-in).

Many health departments or schools of public health may also offer free CHES® credits. One source of low-cost CHES® credits that we have used is www.healthedpartners.org/continuing_education.html. (DISCLOSURE: We received no compensation for this mention. We are simply fans.)

OBTAINING THE ADVANCED-LEVEL CREDENTIAL (MASTER CERTIFIED HEALTH EDUCATION SPECIALIST)

Once you have served as a CHES® for at least 5 years, you may consider upgrading your credential to a Master Certified Health Education Specialist (MCHES®). MCHES® are much less common than CHES®—in 2015, only 170 people registered to take the MCHES® exam, though that number has been steadily growing over the past 3 years. According to NCHEC, an MCHES® is an advanced-level practitioner that has:

1. Met required academic qualifications
2. Worked in the field for a minimum of 5 years
3. Passed a competency-based examination administered by the NCHEC
4. Satisfied the continuing education requirement to maintain the national credential

Becoming an MCHES® takes additional time, energy, and work. You have to have been practicing as a health educator for at least 5 years in a paid capacity (volunteer time does not count). The 5 years of professional practice do not have to be consecutive years—part-time and nonconsecutive service counts. If you have been a CHES® for 5 years, you are qualified to take the exam. If you have not been a CHES® for 5 years but do have the required education AND 5 years of experience working as a health educator, you may qualify.

The MCHES® examination is a criterion-referenced test that contains 165 multiple choice items; 150 of the items are used for the total score and there are 15 pilot items. The MCHES® examination is offered in paper-and-pencil format at college campuses throughout the United States. While there are approximately 130 testing sites currently registered, any campus with a testing service is eligible to become a testing site.

The Seven Areas of Responsibility for Health Education Specialists are the same for the MCHES®, but the percentage of questions for each responsibility differs. The following is the MCHES® examination blueprint based on the Health Educator Job Analysis Study and the percentages of questions by the Seven Areas of Responsibility for Health Education Specialists.

Area of Responsibility for Health Education Specialists	Percent of Questions on MCHES® Exam
Assess needs, resources, and capacity for health education/promotion	10
Plan health education/promotion	16
Implement health education/promotion	15
Conduct evaluation and research related to health education/promotion	20
Administer and manage health education/promotion	18
Serve as a health education/promotion resource person	12
Communicate, promote, and advocate for health and the profession of health education/promotion	9

As you can see, the MCHES® exam focuses more on conducting evaluation and research related to health education/promotion and on administering and managing health education/promotion than does the CHES® exam.

FINAL THOUGHTS

We hope this study guide has been helpful to you as you prepare for your CHES® exam. For us, being a CHES® and then MCHES® has been critical in our professional journeys. We believe it is a credential that demonstrates a commitment to health education, communication, equity, and service. We look forward to having you join the ranks of those who value the work of health educators. Truly, the future of the field has never looked better.

Welcome to the ranks of CHES®!

Index